THE
HOLY COW
and other
Indian Stories

Published by Prakash Books India Pvt. Ltd
113/A, Daryaganj, New Delhi 110002, India
Tel.: 91-11- 2324 7062-65. Fax: (011) 23246975
E-mail: sales@prakashbooks.com
www.prakashbooks.com

Reprint: 2016
1st Edition: 2002
2nd Edition: 2008

Maps and Illustrations by: Tarun Chopra
Miniature Paintings courtesy: Channi Textiles
Silver Tantric Figure courtesy: Gem Palace

Text edited by: Roger Alexander
Designed by: Yogesh Suraksha Design Studio.
www.ysdesignstudio.com

ISBN : 978-81-7234-042-1

Printed & Bound at: Thomson Press (India) Ltd.

THE
HOLY COW
and other
Indian Stories

TARUN CHOPRA

Prakash Books

TO MY PARENTS
LATE SHRI. NARINDER NATH CHOPRA
SMT. CHAND CHOPRA

CONTENTS

THE HOLY COW

A devotee paying obeisance to the holy cow or Gau Mata in Tarkeshwar temple in Jaipur *(above)*; a sacred fountain depicting the Gaumukh at Galtaji near Jaipur *(opp page center)*; common sight on the Indian streets *(opp page below)*

Travelling on Indian roads can be as impressionable an experience as visiting the country's magnificent monuments, seeing its breathtaking natural beauty and admiring the workmanship of its artisans, whose skills have been handed down from one generation to the next. Indeed, for a visitor, driving on Indian roads is a hair-raising experience, with motorized vehicles, animal-drawn wagons and human-powered handcarts competing with each other to get from Point A to Point B.

The former US ambassador to India, Daniel Moynihan, called it "functional anarchy". In fact, he couldn't have been more accurate. If in the States people stick to the right lane and in Britain keep to the left, in India they seem to drive everywhere. And pedestrians be damned. Of course, street-smart as they are brought up to be, pedestrians in India too, contribute their mite to make the chaos worse confounded. For example, given the unruly nature of the traffic, people never look for a zebra crossing (even if there is one it is to decorate the street). And, if visitors were to think that motorists would stop for them merely because they're crossing the road on a zebra crossing, they're in for a nasty surprise — in India, traffic stops for no one. Not even on a zebra crossing. It's like being a jungle out there, even without the zebras.

So, the golden rule while crossing Indian roads is to first look right, then left and then run for dear life across the street, before some-one or something knocks you over. It's like being a player in a computer game. The only difference is that this is not virtual reality but the real thing. No wonder Indians seem to have such a profound belief in reincarnation, or life after death.

Bang in the middle of this mad-house, strolls a serene creature oblivi-ous to the bedlam around it. This is the Holy Cow. (And as holy things go in India, women and cows are venerated in equal measure).

For most cows, the place to be is in the middle of the street. They herd at traffic lights, in all likelihood mislead-ing you into believing that they're there to assist the traffic cop! Of course, that's only half-true. So, really, what are the cows doing in the middle of Indian roads? Why aren't they on farms where they belong? Of course, they're not suffering from the Mad Cow Disease. But there is a method in their apparent madness. As recent studies have dem-onstrated, Indian cows seem to prefer hanging around on busy roads because the exhaust fumes from the smoke belching buses (and trucks, auto-rick-shaws and tractors) seem to discourage flies, while the toxic fumes get them high. Now, that's a typical Indian solution to a vexed problem.

In India, all animals are sacred, even though the people's attitude towards them may lead you to believe otherwise. And in the pan-theon of these sacred creatures, the cow stands heads and shoulders above the rest. Referred to as Gau Mata or Mother Cow, this gentle bovine occupies a special niche in the Indian psyche.

Much before the Pharaohs built the Pyramids or Hammurabi devised laws or the Chinese invented paper, Indians had given up a nomadic existence — which was still the hallmark of the Afri-can, European, American and other

Asian people — and developed an agriculture-based civilization which supported not only neighboring cities but empires. And though maharajas had started to mint coins, which were circulated in cities and used mainly by traders, money had not come into vogue in the countryside, where wealth was determined by the number of cows that a family possessed.

So, the humble cow became legal tender — exchanged for goods and services, proudly presented as dowry at

weddings and reluctantly given away to meet tax obligations. And Gaudan, gifting cows to Brahmin priests, was considered the most pious ceremony of all, since salvation was guaranteed, ersatz 'karma' as it were.

Besides keeping the taxman at bay, adorning a daughter's trousseau, or taking care of the monthly bills, the cow's milk was the main source of nourishment for the country's vast population. Moreover, the cow sustained the economy in more ways than one. Indeed, its dung is used as fuel even today. Cow-dung mixed with hay is fashioned into patties and after being sun-dried warms not only hearth and home, but also keeps the kitchen fire burning for nearly three-quarters of India's rural populace. Cow-dung mixed with clay is wunder-material used for plastering huts, which makes it easy to sweep floors and acts as an effective

A traditional miniature painting showing cattle decorated for a festive occasion *(opp page)*; a woman praying to 'Nandi' the bull, Shiva's favourite mode of transportation *(opp page below)*; a cow browsing in a Jaisalmer street *(left)*; a traffic sign advising drivers to 'Relax' in the chaotic traffic *(below)*

insecticide as well. No wonder the eco-friendly, cost-effective cow dung has been the rage down the centuries in this part of the world!

However, since Indian's are by-and-large vegetarian (and beef, certainly is a big No-No), the cow, given its holier-than-thou status, has rarely been exploited for its meat. But the flip side of the cow's ritualistic position means that no sooner than it stops producing milk, its owner finds it politically correct to abandon the unfortunate creature on the streets, rather than pack it off to the slaughterhouse. Hindus also believe that should a cow tethered in their home die, its owner has to perforce undertake a pilgrimage to all the holy cities of India to atone for the sin. And upon his return, he has to feed the Brahmins in his village. Rather than be laid low by a double-whammy, as it

were, letting the cows loose on the streets is an altogether agreeable and cost-effective option.

Indeed, once out on the streets, cows hardly starve. Every time a meal is cooked in a Hindu house-hold, the first roti (unleavened bread), is left out especially for a cow to consume. And if a cow is spotted on the street, it is called to the door and fed various delicacies prepared to propitiate the gods. On auspicious days of the Hindu calendar, wandering cows are offered sweets and grass as an act of piety.

According to mythology, Lord Vishnu's eighth incarnation (there have been nine so far), was Lord Krishna, who grew up in a pastoral family. While tending to his herd of cows, he would play the flute to keep them happy. This is why he is also referred to as Gopal — one who looks after cows. No wonder the caring of cows enjoys religious

sanctity. Indeed, in one of the most ancient sacred Hindu texts — the Puranas — it is said that among the precious things that came forth from the churning of the seas of creation was the Kamdhenu, the cow that fulfills all desires. Indians believe that every cow is a Kamdhenu.

No wonder there are thousands of tales extolling the importance of the cow. One of the more popular ones tells us about a powerful king in the ancient kingdom of Patliputra, who had everything — wealth, fame, wisdom. But the only thing lacking in this mighty king's life was a son, an heir to his throne. So, when the desire for a son overwhelmed him, the king asked his queen to accompany him on a visit to their Guru who lived deep in the jungle.

The Guru, who was blessed with supernatural powers, immediately understood the reason for the king's visit. "Your Majesty," he informed the king, "once while you were returning from the temple after saying your prayers, you ignored a Kamdhenu cow standing outside the temple. That cow had magical powers. Now, if you are to beget a son, you will have to look after a cow." The king agreed whole-heartedly. "There is lot of merit in looking after cows. I will look after any cow you ask me to," the king replied. The Guru then directed him, "Look after that cow which is as white as milk."

And so it was that the king devoted all his energies in looking after a white cow at the Guru's ashram. He would take it out to the pasture in the morning and stay with it till dusk. He fed the cow, gave it water and kept the flies away. On his return to the ashram in the evenings, the queen would take over, feeding it grass, giving it water and offering it prayers every morning and evening. She would light oil lamps, burn incense sticks and bring fresh flowers from the bushes nearby. The king would sleep on the floor of the shed, next to the cow. Weeks passed and the royal couple continued to devote themselves to caring for the cow.

A day came, when while grazing, a tiger attacked the cow. Seeing this, the king was shattered. He folded his hands before the tiger and requested it to leave the cow alone. The tiger replied, "Your Majesty, I serve Goddess Durga and must have my prey." The king fell on his knees and pleaded with the tiger to spare the cow and have his life instead. Seeing his devotion, the goddess showered the king with flowers and the cow — for it was a Holy Cow — spoke up,

"My Lord, stand up. The tiger was merely an illusion created by me to test your devotion." The cow then asked the king and the queen to drink some milk as a sacred offering and within a year they were blessed with a son.

Such tales are plentiful and the tradition of cow worship is kept alive the cow that is considered sacred in India. The monkey, the cobra, the bull and the peacock are other creatures that are revered by Hindus since each one of them is associated with one god or another.

But the cow occupies pride of place. So much so, that even today

Cows are an integral part of India. They come in various shapes and sizes, decorating the lanes in the cities as well as the highways.
A newspaper report states the intention of a group to have the cow declared the national animal *(below)*

even to this day.

Another reason why the cow is considered sacred is based on the belief that Hindus can reach heaven only after crossing a mythological river by holding the tail of a cow. Besides, the ceremony for the passage of a dead man's soul to heaven includes the donation of a cow to a Brahmin priest.

It is sentiments such as these that have ensured that the cow is treated with respect in Hindu society. It isn't only

there are scores of organizations devoted to 'cow protection'. Only recently, many of these groups have joined hands to demand from the government that India's national animal, the tiger, be replaced by the cow! In years to come the authorities may well be cowed into submission ◆

VHP wants cow as national animal

SHARAD GUPTA
NEW DELHI, DEC 15

THE Vishwa Hindu Parishad (VHP) has Chock the tiger, pick the cow. And they want to in their campaign.

The Sangh outfit wants to strip the poor tional animal. They want that distinction to go

The demand will figure prominently at anna Mahakumbha to be organised on Red Fort ground, VHP leaders are also likely to take up the issue at the three-d ng of their apex body, Margdarshak Mandal at Rameswaram starting January 7.

The Parishad not only wants cow to replace tiger as the national animal but also demands complete closure of mechanised abattoirs and ban on export of meat to protect cow. VHP leaders are confident of roping in various social and religious groups like Jain Samaj, Hindu Mahasabha and the Shiv Sena to build a mass movement. "No Hindu can dare to oppose our demand to save cow," said a senior VHP leader.

The move is likely to create fresh problems for the Atal Behari Vajpayee government especially from its coalition partners, after the recent controversy over Ram Temple issue in Ayodhya.

The Bajrang Dal too at its three-day executive meeting beginning from January 18 in Bhopal, would vigorously take up the demand for declaration of cow as national animal. The meeting will be presided over by former CBI director, Joginder Singh, a VHP leader said.

ARRANGED MARRIAGES

Unlike people in the West, Indians take the institution of marriage very, very seriously. South of the Himalayas, boys and girls don't meet in a fairy tale setting, date each other, fall in love and decide on tying the knot. Of course, things are changing now, but quick-fix weddings are still rare in India for there is more to marriage than a couple exchanging vows.

In India, a boy may even date a girl (or vice versa) for years, but when it comes to taking the plunge, everything — from religion, caste and sub-caste, economic status, language, eating habits and even horoscopes — must match. If it doesn't, that's the end of what may have been a Mills and Boon love story. And there's no solution either. It is essential to employ the services of relatives, friends, neighbours, genealogists, priests and as-

A miniature painting depicting a newly-wedded couple's first night together *(above)*; a traditional horoscope, Janampatri, essential to determine the right partner *(below left)*; matrimonial advertisements in newspapers and on billboards *(opp page)*

trologers, before it can be proclaimed that the boy and girl are fit to be man and wife for ever after. This is one reason why the divorce rate in India is the lowest in the world.

Visitors should not be surprised to see the Sunday newspapers in India carry thousands of matrimonial advertisements, euphemistically titled 'News You Can Use'! Since marriage is serious business, the ads are neatly organized under two main heads — 'Wanted Brides' and 'Wanted Grooms' specifying the religion, region, caste and sub-caste, profession, Manglik or those born under the planetary influence of Mars (this is a tricky one) of the partner sought. In recent times, two more categories — NRI (Non-resident Indian) and Cosmopolitan — have come into vogue among the young upwardly mobile urban youth. But this modern category is minuscule. The vast majority, including the highly educated, is still tied down by tradition for a variety of reasons.

According to Indian law, it is illegal to discriminate on the basis of religion or caste. But the reality is that most people subscribe to the caste system. Caste is important at all stages of a Hindu's life and more so when you (or your parents) decide it's time to get married and raise a family. In an urban environment, matters regarding caste are beginning to matter less and less, but in the villages, where eighty per cent of India lives, it is still considered very important.

India's ancient sacred texts list four main castes — the Brahmins (priests), Kshatriyas (warriors including the ruling aristocracy), Vaishyas (traders) and Shudras (untouchables who performed menial tasks). These main castes then get delineated into scores of sub-castes or denominations. India is also home to many ancient tribes but these ancient people have, over the centuries, become subservient to the caste system for they are outside its pale.

However, as India takes its first steps in the new millennium, caste barriers are slowly breaking down among the urban, educated youth and the matrimonial ads give a clear indication of how Indians rank different professions in the 'marriage market' (a term commonly used in India). There are some jobs that seem to enjoy a premium position — businessmen, doctors, engineers, civil servants (bureaucrats), army, navy, air force, MBAs, architects. Parents play a very important role in family affairs, they tend to

those born under the influence of Mangal (Mars).

Non-resident Indians are part of the great Diaspora who still retain their ties with the Motherland. However, though they may have made other countries their home for a few generations, when a child in the family comes of marriageable age, they look to India

Much before the wedding festivities start, the birds is decorated with jewellery from head to toe as seen in a Mughal miniature painting (above); the groom arrives at the bride's house astride a mare (opp page top); and wedding guests arrive at Gurmehar Majithia's wedding (opp page below). These are some typical motifs of an Indian wedding

arrange the marriage of their children usually within the same professional group. For example, a doctor's son usually studies medicine and may, in all likelihood, marry a lady doctor.

Of the various categories mentioned above, readers may want to know more about the NRI and Manglik, i.e.

— and the matrimonial ads — for the right spouse. These arrangements are entered into because every Indian family seeks an alliance within the milieu of the same cultural background. For those in India who have not migrated overseas, NRI also represents the New Rich Indian and is, therefore, considered extremely eligible. However, a new social angst is being expressed among Indian expats, especially in North America, where educated, professional Indians and their families find themselves at the crossroads of two cul-

Most newspaper ads receive a tremendous response — literally hundreds of letters accompanied by comprehensive backgrounds and references of both the person-to-be-wed as well as the families. The liberal use of adjectives like 'smart', 'well-placed', 'five-figure salary' for would-be grooms and 'homely', 'teetotaler', 'good family background', 'convent-educated', 'wheatish complexion' for would-be brides are de rigueur to paint the otherwise dull individuals in the brightest of hues.

tural influences. That's why they are sometimes cruelly referred to as ABCDs – American Born Confused Desis (natives).

The janampatri (horoscope) plays a pivotal role in matchmaking. A horoscope is drawn based on the time of the birth of the child, complete with details of planetary positions and their influence. A horoscope also lists 36 gunas, or qualities, for each person. During matchmaking, the priests try and match the maximum qualities between the horoscopes of the two people to chart the course of their marriage.

The star-crossed Manglik is another interesting classification in the matrimonial subcategories. Mangliks are those who have Mars, considered unlucky, as their ruling planet. It is best for one Manglik to marry another Manglik for a mismatched couple is supposed to come to grief sooner rather than later.

More often than not, the parents or family elders, not the prospective partners, do the matchmaking and manage talks with the 'opposite side'. If the parents feel the negotiations are going well, the couple at the center of the exercise are permitted to meet in the company of their families in either house, in a restaurant, or even in a temple. Such meetings are usually dispensed with under an hour. Quite expectedly for the embarrassed couple, the conversation follows more or less a set pattern.

Boy: "Namaste!"

Girl: (Looking down demurely and whispering)

Boy: "Where did you study?"

Girl: "HR College."

Neena, an Indian bride in her wedding makeup and ornaments waiting patiently for the marriage rituals to take place *(above);* a groom's party wends its way to the bride's house *(left);* Gurmehar and Saby Majithia tie the nuptial knot *(opp page)*

Boy: "What subject?"
Girl: "English Honours."
Boy: "What are your hobbies?"
Girl: "Cooking, painting and embroidery."
Boy: "Music?"
Girl: "Yes."
Boy: "What do you read?"
Girl: "Mills and Boon."

(The girl, of course, hardly gets a chance to ask too many questions.)

While the more emancipated families now let the couple go out on a 'lunch date' in a restaurant, most others usually end up deciding in favor, or against, on the basis of the brief tête-à-tête in the presence of chaperons. While the bride or groom's approval is sought, parents have the final word. In case the matchmaking does not work, one of the families sends a message across that the couple's astrological charts did not jell.

The earthy villagers, however, avoid this time-consuming exercise. The elders of the family arrange the match among themselves and the intended bride and groom are offered no choice in the matter. Should a girl or boy of marriageable age decide on their own to marry someone they love outside their caste, the family is ostracized by the rest of the village. And given the importance of such issues in the rural areas, this can be particularly devastating.

If everyone concerned agrees to the match, the pact is celebrated with an exchange of gifts. The next step is the contentious issue of the dowry to be paid by the bride's family, though this is discouraged by law. Traditionally, a dowry was what a daughter carried to her husband's home as her share of her inheritance from her father. But over the centuries, this system has come to be abused to such an extent that the groom's family demands what they feel their boy is 'worth'. Indeed, it is not uncommon to read newspaper reports of brides being harassed and, sometimes, even killed for bringing insufficient dowry. This is usually touted as an accident in the kitchen. However women's groups in the cities have become extremely vigilant and offenders now find themselves being punished.

The burden of spending on everything from the dowry to a lavish wedding is the cost the bride's father has to bear. No wonder, in many cases he ends up neck-deep in debt.

However, if the negotiations fructify, a family priest (always a Brahmin) is summoned to set the date of the wedding. After calculating the position of the planets and stars and depending on whether the gods are 'awake' or 'sleeping' the auspicious date and time is set for the big day. Some periods of the year are considered more favorable than others and the family postpones every other business to ensure that the wedding ceremony starts and ends within this time frame.

Invitation cards with images of Lord Ganesha, the Hindu god who brings good luck, are printed and distributed by hand to ensure that those invited are made to feel important. The number of invitees depends upon the social and economic status of the family and could range from fifty to five thousand. The wedding ends up being fun for everyone except for the bride and groom who have to endure hours of tedious rituals.

The groom arrives at the venue of the wedding astride a white mare in gold embroidered livery. The groom's party is accompanied by a loud, usually off-key, brass band belting out popular Hindi film tunes. The groom's family and friends virtually dance their way to the bride's home where the ceremony usually takes place. Known as the 'baraat' (wedding entourage), the procession is received at the venue by the bride's family with garlands according to traditional custom.

The venue is decorated with flowers and fairylights. The groom wears an 'achkan' or long coat with a Mandarin collar, while the bride is dressed in red

'sari' or 'lehnga' (traditional costumes) embroidered with real gold thread and is loaded with fine gold jewellery.

The groom and bride meet on a raised platform where they exchange 'varmalas' (matrimonial garlands). Her sisters, cousins and friends, all of them resplendent in silks and jewellery, accompany the bride. The couple seeks the blessings of their elders and friends on this dais. Meanwhile, a splendid meal is served and the couple eats only after all the other guests have finished.

The actual wedding ceremony takes place at an auspicious hour — only after most of the guests have left — in the company of only close family and friends. Called the 'pheras', the ritual involves the couple circling a holy fire seven times in the ancient Aryan tradition while the family priest recites Vedic hymns and invites the gods to witness the wedding. The couple sits on one side of the fire, the other three occupied by their parents and the priest. The wedding is considered solemnized after the last of seven rounds of the holy fire, accompanied by the chanting of mantras and showering of rose-petals, are over.

The ceremony takes anything from an hour-and-a-half to three hours. Immediately thereafter, it's time for the bride to say goodbye to her family and since she is moving to a stranger's home, there is a good deal of weeping and breast-beating at this stage. Sometimes, professional 'weepies' are hired to highlight the sense of loss the bride's family wants to publicly demonstrate. Since

women are still financially dependent on the men in their lives, the departure ceremony includes the bride saying goodbye to the house in which she grew up but to which she will never return as a member of that family for

she has been given away to someone else. The newly-weds, along with the groom's family, depart in a flower-decorated car or palanquin called the 'doli'. By this time, both the bride and the groom are exhausted and wilting under the weight of their splendid costumes. In all probability, the groom has been playfully bullied by members of the bride's family to whom he will have to pay a 'ransom' to get his shoes back (taken off during the ceremony in front of the holy fire). The whole process is

arrival, another set of rituals are performed and then the couple are accompanied to a room where a bed, sprinkled with rose and jasmine petals, has been especially prepared for them. Here, to the accompaniment of good-natured rib-aldry, they are left alone, probably for the last time in their lives.

A glass of milk laced with aphrodi-siacs is placed by the bedside for the groom. Known as 'suhaag raat', the first night as husband and wife, an

An emotionally charged moment for the new bride who leaves her parent's house after the wedding ceremony. The bride is taken in a decorated palanquin or automobile to her husband's home where she enters a new phase in her life as she has to 'adjust' with a man and his extended family she hardly knows

so long and so slow that it is no wonder that the groom often jokes that he would not undergo the ceremony ever again in his life.

It is usually the wee hours of the morning by the time the groom reaches home with his new bride. On

extensive culture is woven around this highly ritualistic consummation of the marriage.

And on the birth of the first child, the entire process of rearing the kid towards marriage begins all over again ◆

THE GREAT
INDIAN BUREAUCRACY

An Indian's life is enmeshed in a bureaucratic tangle — whether its the electricity utility or the telephone office. Live wire electricity distribution box in Delhi sums up the state of the basic utilities like electricity and telephone *(left and below)*. India boasts of worlds best software professionals, but it takes hours just to get on line. typist waiting for clients to make official documents *(opp page)*

If there was an Olympic gold medal for cutting through Red Tape any Indian would win it by a mile. Indeed, thanks to the great Indian bureaucracy, the citizens of the largest democracy in the world have become world beaters in the art of cutting through Red Tape, for here we have to cut it lengthwise!

For anyone visiting our great country, the whacky ways of the bureaucracy are evident right at the airport where there are slow-moving queues to get various documents, non-documents, baggage tags, etc. rubber stamped for no rhyme or reason. While visitors may be forgiven for trying to decipher why in God's name everything has to be rubber-stamped, consider the plight of ordinary mortals who have to run the gauntlet to obtain even the most basic of facilities.

THE CASE OF THE DEAD TELEPHONE

Let me tell you about my brush with this great monolith known as the Government of India when I attempted to get my telephone transferred from one address to another. About three years ago, I shifted from Greater Kailash to Sainik Farms, two residential areas in New Delhi not very far apart. I wrote to the telephone exchange well in advance of the move hoping to have the telephone working when I moved into my new house. However, the great Indian bureaucracy had other things in mind.

If my telephone is still not working, it is because I did not follow the RULES. Silly me, I had made my request for the transfer on my personal stationery. Apparently, the application has to be submitted on the prescribed form.

So when I learned about it, I filled out the required form and waited for the phone to ring. No such luck. Inevitably, I found myself squashed in a queue of sweaty, smelly bodies waiting to see the commercial officer, the demigod who okays such important files. When I finally got to him, it was only to learn that since the telephone had

the doors of the powers that be at the telephone exchange. But to get there, I had to first stand in a queue to get a gate pass, an entry permit to gain access into the building. For this, my name address, telephone number (in my case N.A — Not Applicable) and the official I wished to meet were noted in a bulky register. The same information was then duly filled out in the small slip of paper (gate pass) that was given to me. This had to be handed over to a half-dozing security man, he in turn skillfully tears a neat hole in the piece of paper as the sign of being used.

taken more than six months to be transferred, it was now a 'DP' (disconnected phone) and I was required to fill another form to get things moving again.

Since there was nothing else to be done, I filled out the appropriate form. And while the phone continued to remain kaput, the file relating to it got thicker and thicker. An eternity passed, but the phone continued to remain in coma.

Soon, I was once again knocking on

Once inside, I asked for directions across a maze of rooms and tables heaped with files, since there were no signs indicating where one had to go. All around me harried visitors seemed to spend all their time sitting in front of rooms, with no officials inside, hoping someone would appear and sign a piece of paper so that they could go up the bureaucratic hierarchy in the hope of getting some minor fault repaired. It was a surreal scene straight out of Kafka.

However, an Indian does not give up hope so easily. Queuing up is an art you learn in India. Indeed, when you find people standing in a queue you believe you should be part of, get in the line and stick to it. If you're lucky, it will turn out to be the right one. If not — and you'll only find out only when you reach at the head

of the queue — find another queue and start all over again. And, maybe, yet again!

Once you make it to the official's room and are lucky to find him in, get to the point by placing your papers right under his nose — don't

The notice board of the utility office where consumers can post their complaints *(above)*; letters to the editor of a newspaper complaining of poor services *(right)*; archaic laws in the age of remote sensing satellites still prohibit photography at all Indian airports *(opp page)*; receipt which enables one to use the video camera *(opp below)*

wait to be summoned, for that is unlikely to happen. When I reached the commercial officer, he told me the telephone was now in the category 'DNP' (dues not paid). I tried to reason that if the telephone was not working, how was it to be billed. A rent, he informed me, is charged for the connection whether the telephone works or not. And I had defaulted on the payment. I tried to point out that despite my attempts, if the telephone was not working, it was because his office had done nothing about it. Tough luck, said the official cheerily, rules are rules.

Finally, having paid the dues and rent as demanded by the telephone company, I managed to get the telephone actually working, but only for a brief while for it was disconnected again. On inquiry, I was informed that it was on account of outstanding bills. I showed them the bills I had paid for the three months the phone had been working. Clearly, the bills had not been paid by the bloke who had been given the number earlier, the official told me. Since I had no intention to clear someone

Wake up, railways

Several letters have appeared in these columns complaining about the huge gap between local trains and the platforms of many stations. But, the railway authorities are yet to respond. The gap has widened after the laying of new sleepers by the railways: While it is appreciated that new sleepers need to be placed to improve safety and speed, is it also not the responsibility of the authorities to ensure that commuters are able to board and alight from the trains safely? I will not be surprised if a commuter falls between the gap of trains and the platforms and is either killed or injured. I hope, the railway authorities will wake up immediately and tackle the problem on a top priority basis.
—*H. Hemant, Ashok Nagar, off Eastern Express Highway, Kurla (east)*

else's bills, I protested. Only to be told to see the accounts officer on the sixth floor.

NO VIDEO!

In India, granting permission to use a video camera at a historical monument has been perfected into a fine art. In order to use camcorder to film a 'protected' monument, one must purchase a ticket for a fee. But to obtain the ticket, a form for permission to use the video camera has to be filled out. The details you enter on this form are then copied on the ticket — in 'duplicate' — and duly stamped. Half of this coupon is then stored in the records of the booking clerk, the other half given to you.

While at most monuments your ordeal ends here, in the case of the Taj Mahal you have to go even further. For, the moment you purchase the required permission, to film your memories of the Taj, a chaperon latches on to you. His task is to ensure you film the majestic monument only from the

entrance platform. Why can't you use the video elsewhere in the Taj? No one seems to know the logic behind this rule.

AIRPORT BLUES

Indian airports are fine examples of poor design least suited to serve their function. To enter the airport, you have to get through a half-open door manned by security personnel who ask to see your ticket while trolleys and baggage block your way. To take a flight, even within the country, you will have to:

Show your ticket to enter the airport.
Get your bags to the X-ray counter.
Unload the cart.
Reload the cart.
Look for the check-in counter.
Check-in.
Collect your boarding card, baggage tag and hand baggage tag.
Get in the queue for the security check.
Get boarding card stamped at two places.
The batteries from your camera may or may not be removed depending on the mood of security personnel. This is also when your hand baggage tag is stamped.

Show your boarding card again to a person who frisks you for concealed weapons.

Now you wait for your flight to be announced. If it is 20-30 minutes late, don't bother, it is considered to be on time. If it is alarmingly late, open a book and enjoy it.

Once the announcement is made informing you of your flight's departure, join the boarding queue at the gate. Show your stamped boarding card and your stamped hand baggage tag. Board a non-air-conditioned bus to transfer you to the aircraft. Join another queue at the aircraft and show your boarding card once again.

Make sure you carry a jacket or woolen sweater while travelling in India for either the air-conditioning is freezing cold or doesn't work at all.

Bon voyage!

DRIVING ME CRAZY

Ten years ago, when I was heading for America for the first time, an international driving license, I was informed, was essential if I intended to use a car there. So off I went in pursuit of one. After making a few inquiries, I soon realized that in order to get an international driving license, I first needed a local one. This took me to the office of the road transport authority and into a maze of queues. I was rescued by a tout or middleman sitting on a scooter, parked under a shady neem tree.

Tout: "What do you want?"
Self: "A driving license."
Tout: "Do you have a learner's?"
Self: "No."
Tout: "Problem, big problem! Everything has to be organized. Medical, age, proof of residence..."
Self: "How much time will it take?"
Tout: "How much can you pay?"
Self: "I need it urgently."
Tout: "For getting it within a week, it'll cost you Rs. 600 (approx. $15)."
Self: "No, I want it today."
Tout: "Rs 2,000 ($50). Four hours only."
Self: "Done."
Tout: "Sign these papers, get a photograph taken under that tent, wait for the driving test over there under the tree."
Self: "I do not have a car."

Tout: "It is just a formality, Sir. He'll ask if you drive; you say Yes."

Self: "When will I get the license?"

Tout: "In four hours."

The longest it took in the whole deal was getting the photograph taken. The rest of it was a cakewalk.

Armed with my new license, I went to get my international driving license. The person in charge gave me a piece of paper and asked me to learn everything on it well for I was to be "tested".

At the examination, I could only re-member two of the thirty-six odd signs. The examiner was totally disgusted with the outcome of the examination. "Very bad, very bad," I was told. "I am going to sign your license, but you must go home and learn all the signs." I thanked him for sign-ing the license and apologized profusely for not being able to learn all the signs.

Driving in India implies getting from one point to another. How you do that is your own problem. Rarely is anyone trained to park, overtake, or drive in one's lane. The lines on the road are for decoration, they don't mean anything to the drivers. The rear view mirror is also rarely used, most of the time it is kept folded. With so much chaos in front of the vehicles, drivers hardly bother to see what is happening at the rear. In fact, the three things you require most on Indian roads are – Good Horn, Good Brakes & Good Luck ◆

THE GREAT MUGHALS

BABUR
Twenty-seven years after the Portuguese landed on the Malabar coast in southwest India (now in the state of Kerala), Babur marched across the plains of Punjab in north India. The heat and dust of the northern plains did not bother him for he coveted the throne of Hindustan (India). Given the sorry state of affairs in the Sultanate of Delhi, which was on its last legs, Babur had no problem reaching the city of Panipat, just 80 km north of Delhi. The only thing that remained in the way of his conquest was the imperial army of Ibrahim Lodhi, who was the then emperor of Hindustan.

At the tender age of twelve, Babur had been crowned king of Ferghana in Uzbekistan. His was an impeccable lineage – in his veins ran the blood of Timur or Tamerlaine on his father's side and the great Mongol, Chengez Khan on his mother's side. Despite his young age, he soon added Samarkand to his kingdom. But the glory was his for only a short while as his cousins plotted against him and finally succeeded in overthrowing him. Ousted, Babur found a foothold in the city of Kabul, which he ruled for a long time.

In Kabul, he saw caravans loaded with silver, gold, silks, ivory and spices coming from India. This aroused his curiosity. He saw an opportunity in the power struggles among the Afghan rulers of north India that led to a vacuum in power.

Now here he was with a small army of 12,000, facing the imperial Afghan army of 1,00,000 plus 1,000 elephants. It did

not take Babur long to realize that he was no match for the Afghans in a conventional battle. To add to his concern, the Afghans seemed in no hurry to attack. Babur called his generals to his tent and asked them to round up all the cattle from the neighboring villages. They would attack at the break of dawn. The

Semi-precious stone inlay decorations at the Taj Mahal *(above);* the coat of arms of the Sisodia Rajputs who refused to surrender to the Mughals *(opp page left);* the ramparts of the Agra Fort *(right);* a Mughal elephant saddle known as the howda *(top right)*

generals couldn't see the use of the cattle in an attack against the mighty elephants, but who was to argue with Babur, known by his epithet, The Tiger.

Of course, Babur had a secret plan that he was unwilling to divulge even to his generals. The cattle were herded together and bundles of straw tied to their backs. As soon as the battle drums began to roll, the hay was lit and the animals pushed towards the imperial Afghan army. By the time the cattle reached the enemy ranks, the fire against their skins was making them behave in an unpredictable fashion. The elephants reacted violently to the beasts and threw off their mahouts, crushed the soldiers who came in their way and created utter confusion. Babur took advantage of the situation and his army swept through the Afghans like a scythe. Ibrahim Lodhi was killed.

Babur marched on to Delhi where he was crowned emperor of Hindustan. He dispatched his son Humayun to take possession of the Afghan treasury in Sikandra, near Agra. In Sikandra, Humayun met the Raja of Gwalior who was seeking refuge there. The Raja begged Humayun to spare his life in exchange for a stone of great value, later called the Kohinoor (mountain of light) diamond. On his return to Delhi, Humayun presented the Kohinoor to Babur returned it to his son. Humayun told his father that he had put aside the most expensive stone in the world. "What is the value of it?" asked Babur. "If sold," said Humayun, "it can feed the whole world for two-and-a-half days." This is the first time the Kohinoor finds mention in history. Eventually, of course, the famous diamond reached the British crown where it was re-cut into three pieces.

Although Babur had defeated Ibrahim Lodhi, he faced imminent danger from the fierce Rajput King, Rana Sanga of Mewar. The king's bravery was legendary. As a result of the many battles he had fought, he had lost an eye and an arm. His right leg was fractured at three places and his body bore the scars of eighty-five wounds. Luckily for Babur, the arrival of the rains offered his battle-fatigued men some respite.

On the eve of the battle against the fiery Rajputs, Babur gathered his men around him and took a wow never to touch alcohol in his life. He declared that the war they were going to fight was jihad, a holy war against the Hindu infidels. These dramatic announcements sent the blood coursing through the Mughal army. The Rana's army was routed, though he managed to elude the Babur. The battle of Khanua established Mughal supremacy.

As emperor of Hindustan, Babur could now relax and pursue his passion for reading literature and composing poetry. His memoirs, the Babur-nama, established a tradition that was followed by all the Mughals.

Babur didn't enjoy the fruits of his victory for very long. Just four years after his Indian conquest, a strange sequence of events unfolded. His son Humayun fell

A rare silver howda *(opp page centre)*; ladies in a Mughal harem *(opp page below)*; the 16th century tomb of the second Mughal emperor Humayun which became a basic model for the Taj *(above)*; a plan of Humayun's tomb in the charbagh (four gardens) layout *(right)*

gravely ill on a visit to Delhi. The hakims (doctors) tried medicines that had no affect on him. One amir (noble) suggested that Babur promise Allah the thing dearest to him in exchange for his son's health. Babur prayed that Allah exchange the emperor's life in place of his son's health. By a coincidence, just such a miracle happened. Humayun recovered but Babur's health began to deteriorate. On December 26, 1530, the Almighty took Babur in his arms. The founder of the Mughal dynasty was first buried in Agra and later shifted to his beloved Kabul, with its cooler climate and musk melons that he had missed so much during his reign in India.

HUMAYUN Babur's death brought Humayun the crown of India and the stark reality that only four years had passed since the battle of Panipat. His first task, therefore, was to suppress rebellions in the newly formed empire and to consolidate it.

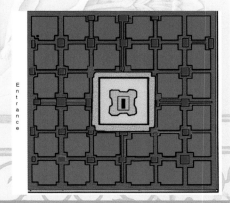

Entrance

Humayun was born in Kabul in 1508. At a young age, he was made governor of an important province, a capable leader, he proved his worth in the battle of Panipat and again in the battle against Rana Sanga of Mewar.

Meanwhile, Sher Shah organized his troops and attacked Humayun. Injured, Humayun had to flee the battlefield and nearly drowned while crossing the Ganga. A bhishti or a water carrier saved his life. He helped Humayun cross the river on an

If Babur's passion had been literature, Humayun was obsessed with astrology and astronomy. Even to govern, he used the help of astrology. Certain matters of state were discussed on only certain days of the week. He even wore colours corresponding with different days of the week.

Later Humayun became involved in his own world of opium and concubines, failing to register the growing threat from an Afghan King, Sher Shah Suri. First Bihar then Bengal fell to the Afghan. When it became clear that the Afghan was no petty rebel, Humayun decided to initiate action.

inflated buffalo skin. As a gesture of his gratefulness, Humayun pronounced the bhishti emperor for one day. (In turn, the bhishti exploited the moment by getting leather coins struck in his name.)

Sher Shah marched to Agra and once again defeated Humayun at Kanauj, forcing the emperor to flee his empire

Akbar, the third Mughal emperor, was the greatest among the six Mughals who ruled India between the 16th and 18th centuries. On the top is ante chamber of his tomb at Sikandra; Akbar's capital Fatehpur Sikri which is now a ghost city *(opp page top and bottom)*; the arched hall of the Diwan-i-Am at the Agra Fort *(opp page center)*; a detail from Sikandra *(right)*

with a handful of his men, treasure and harem. On reaching Sindh, he was offered shelter by a Hindu Raja. It was here, in Amarkot, that a son was born to him and Hamida Bano Begum, his wife. Humayun named the child Jalaluddin Muhammad Akbar. Leaving his family behind, Humayun and his brother journeyed to Persia where Shah Tahmash received him as the emperor of Hindustan, though his real status was that of a refugee. Humayun enjoyed the Shah's hospitality so much, he seemed reluctant to return to Hindustan.

But return he did after a freak accident brought an end to Sher Shah's life. A bomb hurled by Sher Shah rebounded and burnt him to ashes. Humayun was able to quite literally walk back to the throne and claim it as his right. Once more he began his pursuit of opium and astrology. One evening, having gazed upon the planet Venus, he was climbing down the steps of the tower when he heard the muezzin calling the faithful to prayer. Humayun kneeled down to pray, but caught his foot in the hem of his robe and stumbled down, succumbing to his fall on the second day – January 26, 1556.

Humayun's death was kept secret till the information could be communicated to his heir and successor, Akbar. The little

boy was crowned emperor of Hindustan in the wheat fields of Punjab.

Humayun's widow built an exquisite tomb in memory of Humayun in Delhi. From then on started the charbagh (literally, four gardens) tomb tradition among the Mughals, that was to culminate eighty years later in the building of the Taj Mahal.

texts translated into Persian and Islamic books translated into Sanskrit. Over 40,000 books were so translated – the Mughals, as a rule, loved manuscripts. His other passion was music and the legendary Indian classical singer Tansen was his court musician. It is said that when Tansen sang at Anup Talo in Fatehpur Sikri, lamps floating in the water would ignite spontaneously. Akbar was also fond of hunting wild animals. Trained cheetahs accompanied him on his expeditions and he became legendary for killing a wounded tigress on foot and bringing under control a 'mast' or intoxicated elephant that moments ago had killed its mahout. He was also interested in night polo, his own invention of the sport,

AKBAR

Akbar was only fourteen when news of his father's death reached him. He was fortunate to have Bairam Khan as his mentor. For two weeks till Akbar's safety was not ensured, Humayun's death was not made public and a stand-in for the emperor appeared daily at the jharokha – a Mughal tradition – till the new emperor was crowned. Short and stocky, Akbar grew up a fearless youth with no formal education. In stark contrast to his father and grandfather, he remained illiterate, but a lack of formal education in no way hampered his quest for knowledge. Each night, when going to bed, there was someone to read to him. Such was his thirst for knowledge that during his reign, he had Indian religious

played with a flaming ball of fire.

Akbar's love for women became only too well known and besides his four wives, he had a harem with over five hundred concubines. Yet, if there was anything he lacked, it was an heir to his throne. While his daughters survived, infant sons had died soon after birth. Disappointed, he made a trip to seek the blessings of the mystic Sufi saint Salim Chisti. The saint prophesied three sons for the emperor and in due time,

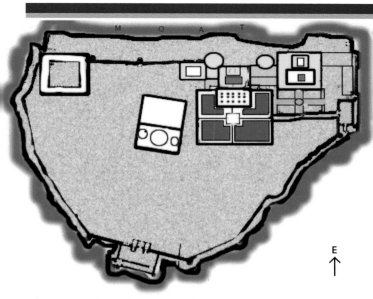

A Mughal miniature showing Akbar receiving his son Jahangir in Agra Fort *(opp page top);* the tomb of sufi saint Salim Chisti at Fatehpur Sikri where people make a wish after tying threads in the lattice windows *(opp page below and this page middle left);* the layout of Agra Fort *(left);* Akbar's tomb at Sikandra *(bottom left)*

E
↑

three sons were born to him. In 1569, Jodha Bai gave birth to a boy who was named Salim in honour of the saint. The child grew up to become Emperor Jahangir.

Akbar, who had made additions to the fort at Agra, now decided to build himself a new capital that he named Fatehpur Sikri. Work started in 1571 and beautiful palaces, gardens and water bodies were constructed. Akbar was so enthused with his new capital that he was seen quarrying the stone alongside his laborers. When completed, Akbar shifted in and lived here for thirteen years. However, the city was abandoned for lack of fresh water. Today, little survives of the city, but the palaces are still there, as magnificent as ever, indicative of Akbar's understanding of architecture.

Although Akbar was illiterate, he had a mystical twist to him. To the horror of the orthodox Muslims of his time, he created the Imabat Khana where religious heads of different religions were asked to carry on discourses on their philosophies. These included Jesuits, Jews and Hindus. It was the first time that a Muslim ruler was seen to have tolerant outlook towards other religions. He removed a tax imposed on non-Muslims called the jizyah and even structured a new religion called Din-i-Ilahi based on the teachings of all faiths.

The Mughal ruling classes' passion for the hunt was also shared by the ladies of the harem *(left)*; Akbar and Jahangir *(below left)*; a medallion design in Itmad-ud-Daulah's tomb *(opp page top)*; a miniature and a manuscript detailing the flora and fauna of India during Jahangir's reign *(opp page)*

Out of all the philosophers who came to Fatehpur Sikri, the Jesuits drew much of Akbar's attention. Led by Catalan Padre Antonio Monserrat in 1580, they must have presented an unusual sight in the Mughal court in their regalia. Akbar proudly wore a lapis-lazuli cross presented by the Jesuits and appointed Padre Monserrat as tutor to Prince Salim.

Akbar's court consisted of nine 'jewels' of various skills, among them Birbal, Todarmal, Bhagwandas and Abul Fazal. By the time Akbar was fifty-eight and still in fine fettle, he had outlived his own son Murad. His other son, Daniyal was an alcoholic. Salim feared his father would outlive him too and so revolted against his father, eliminating Abul Fazal, Akbar's most trusted friend in the struggle. This enraged Akbar

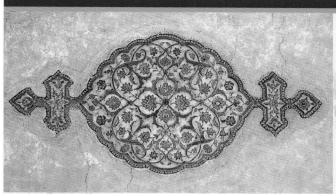

Mughal emperors passed away. Sikandra, near Agra, was to be his final home. Here he lies buried in a magnificent tomb. Later, the Jats looted the wealth of the tomb, but it is still a pleasant site with blackbucks and monkeys in its gardens.

and it took Hamida Bano Begum to bring about a truce between son and grandson. In 1604, Hamida Bano Begum passed away. This broke the emperor's will to live too. In 1605, on October 25, the greatest of the

Birbal's porridge: Emperor Akbar was the greatest of the Mughal kings who ruled India from the 16th to the 18th century. Well known for his tolerance, he appointed various Hindu noblemen to his cabinet, among them Raja Birbal who was popular for his wit and practical humor. Akbar and Birbal would often find themselves in situations where the courtier was able to outwit the emperor.

Now it so happened that one cold December night, with the season of shikar behind them, the emperor thought up an amusing sport. He sent out messengers to announce that he was prepared to pay a thousand gold coins to anyone who was able to stand all night in the freezing waters of the river Jamuna that flowed below the ramparts of his palace. The news of the challenge spread like wildfire and thousands of hopefuls turned up on the fateful day.

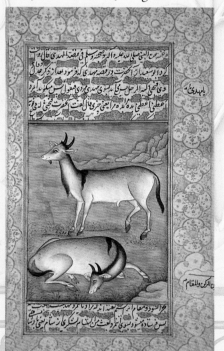

Contestants prepared themselves by applying a thick coat of oil, which they hoped, would keep out the cold. But as the night grew, the temperature started to fall sharply and soon, to the amusement of the royal family, they started to come out of water. Finally, only a handful of bodybuilders were left in the water, along with a thin, emaciated looking washer man or dhobi. Soon, the bodybuilders left too and only the skinny dhobi and Sher Khan, the wrestling champion of Agra, were left to compete for the prize. Popular feeling was that Sher Khan would win, but by 4:30 am, even he could not bear the cold and it was left to the dhobi to await the first rays of dawn.

Akbar summoned the dhobi to the Diwan-i-Am or hall of public audience. "My dear man," the emperor of India asked him, "how did you outlast the strongest man in the city?" "My lord," said the dhobi, "when I was standing in the freezing waters of the Jamuna, I saw a lamp burning in your palace. Gazing on it and thinking of the warmth it provides, helped me to survive the bitter cold."

The emperor's courtiers, unable to stomach the fact that a commoner was walking away with the fabulous prize money, filled the emperor's ears with doubts, saying the warmth from the palace lamp amounted to disqualification. The emperor withdrew the prize and the poor dhobi was shown the way out. But it disappointed Birbal to see him to see how easily the emperor had given credence to the hanger's-on. He slipped out of the Diwan-i-Am without a word.

Next day, when Birbal did not show up at court, Akbar dispatched a messenger to his house. He returned to inform the emperor that Birbal would be back as soon as he had finished cooking khichri, a porridge of rice and lentils. The next day, Birbal was again missing - he was still cooking his khichri, the messenger explained. Another day passed. Annoyed, Akbar decided he would personally go to Birbal's house to sort out the problem.

On reaching Birbal's house, Akbar demanded to where the minister was. "My lord, he is cooking khichri on the roof," came the reply. On the roof, Akbar saw Birbal busy fussing with a pot. "What are you doing, Raja

out the fire?" shouted Akbar, who by now was visibly upset. "Sir, for fire, I have been pointing the pot towards the lamp in your palace, but the dish is still not ready."

Akbar understood what his wily minister was trying to tell him. Hailing Birbal as a pillar of truth and justice, Akbar summoned the dhobi back to his court and handed him the prize he deserved.

Birbal?" Akbar demanded. "Cooking khichri, my lord," replied his minister without taking his eyes off the pot. "Three days to cook one pot of rice! Are you in your senses or has opium addled your brain?" cried Akbar. "My great lord, emperor of Hindustan, I have been trying to cook the rice with lentils in the pot..." "Where is the fire my good man? How can you cook with-

JAHANGIR

Jahangir was 30 when he was crowned emperor. Akbar had consolidated and strengthened his empire, leaving Jahangir free to the vices of wine and opium. Unlike his brothers who succumbed to them, Jahangir somehow survived. He also had a rebellious streak in him, as a young prince, he had become infatuated with a dancer called Anarkali and announced his intention of marrying her. When Akbar refused permission, young Salim took up his sword against the might of the empire. It was only on Jodha Bai's intervention that the prince's rebellion was overlooked. Finally, with the help of her father, the Maharaja of Amber, Jahangir's mother ensured the disappearance forever, of Anarkali. But

Since the Mughals missed their home in Fergana, they brought it closer by decorating the walls of their palaces in India with flowers, rose water sprinklers and incense burners. These motifs are well preserved in the 17th Century tomb of Itmad-ud-Daulah in stone inlay and wall paintings

the romantic Jahangir was to become besotted by yet another woman who, as his wife Nur Jahan, would become the de facto ruler of Hindustan.

The Jesuits managed Jahangir's early education but Christianity made no impression on him. One reason why Jahangir liked the Jesuits was for the European paint-

ings they were able to procure for him. In the paintings of the time, he is shown with a painting of the Madonna. While he himself showed no inclination towards Christianity, he had three nephews baptised to make the Jesuits happy. On the other hand, Jahangir was fascinated by sadhus, fakirs and other ascetics, admiring their life on the fringes of society.

While Akbar preferred to dress ordinarily in cottons, in the words of Sir Thomas Roe, the English ambassador, Jahangir was fashionable. "Clothes laden with diamonds, rubies, pearls...his head, neck, breast and arms all had precious stones..." The jewels would change with each court appearance. However, when it came to eating, his tastes were simpler. He liked the poor man's khichri, camel's milk and rohu fish. Mangoes were his favorite fruit.

Jahangir was a keen naturalist and possessed a scientific temperament. His court painter Mansur was commissioned to paint only birds and animals. Of Mansur's surviving twenty-four paintings, twenty-two are in the collection of the Maharaja of Jaipur. A connoisseur of miniature paintings, the art reached its zenith during his reign. By just looking at a painting, Jahangir could identify its artist. In the vale of Kashmir, he laid the famous Shalimar gardens against the backdrop of the Himalayas. These and other gardens are just as beautiful today as in the Mughal times.

When the increase in his consumption

of alcohol threatened his health, Jahangir's solution was typical: he reduced the intake of wine by doubling his dose of opium, adding marijuana occasionally. Politically, Jahangir inherited a stable kingdom and was free to indulge his vices. But typically for the Mughals, his son Khusrau rebelled against him and Jahangir had him blinded and consigned to jail. The nobles who had helped Khusrau in his act of rebellion were

ting beside Jahangir in durbar (court). He was offered the governorship of the cash rich province of Gujarat.

This honeymoon between father and son did not last long. What concerned Shah Jahan most was the emperor's failing health and he did not want to be too far from Agra when the battle of succession broke out in the event of his death. Therefore, when Shah Jahan ignored Jahangir's

stitched up in a garment made from freshly killed cow skins and paraded through the bazaar of Agra. The heat dried the skin, making it shrink, painfully killing the traitors. Such harsh measures served to discourage any future, potential threats. Jahangir's other son, Prince Khurram proved successful in his campaigns in the Deccan (modern Hyderabad) and in Mewar (Udaipur). This earned him the title of Shah Jahan, 'ruler of the world' and the honor of sit-

orders to march to Afghanistan, Empress Nur Jahan, in control of the affairs of the empire, interpreted it as a revolt. She led a campaign against Shah Jahan where he was discredited in the battlefield. Nur Jahan's real name was Mehrunnisa. She was the daughter of a Persian noble, Ghias Beg. The Mughal empire looked towards Persian culture for inspiration and even used Persian as a court language. Ghias Beg had the title of Itmad-ud-Daula, the pillar of the empire, in the state. His daughter Mehrunnisa was the lady-in-waiting for Jahangir's stepmother. Jahangir chanced upon her in the zenana and was bewitched by her. Even though she married someone else, Jahangir made her his wife after her husband died in a hunting accident. Upon their marriage, he bestowed the title of Nur Jahan 'light of the world', upon her.

Not only was Nur Jahan beautiful, she was also vivacious and a trendsetter when it came to designing everything from costumes to jewellery and even carpets. A hostess without parallel, she was an excellent shot, a companion to her husband and a source of great political intrigue. As de facto ruler, court documents and coins bore her seal. Along with the increase in her power, her father and brother too became powerful. When her father died in 1622, Nur Jahan designed and built the beautiful mausoleum, Itmad-ud-Daula, in his memory. Shah Jahan,

her stepson, married Mumtaz Mahal (later known as lady of the Taj), her niece. But Nur Jahan's ultimate game plan was to have her daughter from her first marriage follow her as empress, as the bride of Jahangir's other son, Prince Shahryar.

On November 7, 1627, when Jahangir passed away, Shah Jahan was in the Deccan. It was opportune for Shahryar to ascend the throne as emperor, but on Shah Jahan's return, Shahryar and all other potential heirs were done to death. On February 6, the following year, Shah Jahan, now thirty-six years old and Jahangir's son by a princess of Jodhpur, ascended the throne of Hindustan.

SHAH JAHAN AND MUMTAZ MAHAL

Prince Khurram was only sixteen years old when he fell in love with Asaf Khan's daughter, Arjuman Bano Begum, later known as Mumtaz Mahal. Shah Jahan and Mumtaz Mahal first met at the Meena Bazaar, a weekly market held in the palace every Friday. Here, the women from noble families would set up stalls for the pleasure of their male buyers from the royal family. Shah Jahan, then known as Prince Khurram, was being carried in a palanquin by four Tartar women slaves when he stopped before a stall where a young girl was selling mishri, crude sugar crystals. The prince picked up a

The beauty of the Taj
mesmerises natives and
tourists alike. No matter
from which angle or
time of day you view it,
this monument of love
is bound to captivate
you. A view of the Taj
from the banks of the
river Yamuna and a
close-up of the inlay and
bas-relief work that
decorates the
monument *(left)*

Shah Jahan, the builder of the Taj, with the princes in the Diwan-i-Am at the Red Fort in Delhi *(left);* details of a bronze door handle *(opp page center);* the deserted Diwan-i-Am with marble throne, arches with bas-relief motifs stand deserted in stark contrast to the to the pomp and gaiety of the Mughal court as seen in the miniature painting *(opp page below)*

piece and asked its price. The girl flirtatiously quoted an astronomical amount. Showing no surprise, the prince paid up in gold coins. Seeing the prince mistake the mishri for a diamond, the girl started laughing and her veil was uncovered to reveal her face. Mesmerized by his stepmother's niece, he vowed to make her his bride.

They were married in 1612 when he was twenty and she was nineteen. In all, she gave birth to fourteen children, averaging one child every sixteen months. Of these, only four boys and three girls survived. Mumtaz Mahal died four years after Shah Jahan's accession to the throne, during the birth of her fourteenth child, in 1631. At that time she was camping with Shah Jahan in Burhanpur. She accompanied the emperor on all his travels and pregnancy did not prevent her from undertaking these journeys, no matter how arduous. It was in the early hours of the morning of June 17, 1631 that a hemor-

rhage caused during the birth of her third daughter, Gauhara Begum, resulted in her death. When news of the queen's condition reached Shah Jahan, he rushed to her side, but it was clear that the empress would not revive. Kneeling beside her, he asked her if there was anything he could do for her. There was, said his dying empress. She made him promise that he would not have any more children from his other wives and that he would build a tomb over her grave that would be so beautiful, it would remind coming generations of the story of their love.

As the empress closed her eyes, a last teardrop slipped out from her beautiful eyes and caressed her cheek. The grief-stricken emperor removed the teardrop from his beloved's face and eventually built her a mausoleum that looked as though it was -

'An eternal teardrop,
Descending from the heaven

On the cheek of time.'

Mumtaz Mahal's body was bathed with cold camphor and rosewater by female bearers and wrapped in five pieces of cloth. Four close relatives carried the body to the burial site. She was temporarily buried in a garden on the banks of the river Tapti, two yards below the earth, her body aligned from north to the south with the face turned west towards the holy city of Mecca. Shah Jahan mourned for forty days. He wore only white. His hair too turned white. He would often visit her grave at night and cry there till the wee hours of the morning. He would hardly eat or listen to music. He refused to enter the women's quarters that would remind him of her. For two years, Shah Jahan was a broken man.

After six months, he had her body transported to Agra, close to the site where she would finally lie. The garden where her tomb was to be built was bought from the Maharaja of Jaipur. The body was buried, again temporarily, in the north west corner of the garden close to the mosque. The final blueprint for the tomb was drawn by leading architects of the empire, Mir Abad al-Karim and Makramat Khan. Ustad Ahmad Lahori is another name connected with many of the Shah Jahan's buildings. The final plan was submitted to Shah Jahan for his approval. After work on it began, sixteen years were to pass before the main building was ready

Shah Jahan in a viewing gallery, or jharokha, at an elephant parade *(left);* a view of the Lahori Gate of the Red Fort from Chandni Chowk in Delhi *(below).* In 1857 the British army marched into the Red Fort and ousted the last Mughal emperor. In 1947, India's independence was declared from the top of this gate

is a synthesis of Hindu and Islamic building traditions. It is certainly the most symmetrical of all Mughal buildings. A walled garden with four water channels is a representation of paradise or Pari Darwaza, abode of the angels. Since Islam as a religion took birth in the desert state of Saudi Arabia, water and gardens are closely associated with heaven. The sacred color for Muslims is also green. The pietra dura inlay on the surface

and another five before the garden and courtyard were completed. Twenty thousand workers, artisans and master-craftsmen worked on the site. A township called Mumtazabad sprang up around the site. Some fifteen hundred elephants transported the white marble blocks, each weighing a ton-and-a-half, to the site. Large numbers of Brahmi bulls were used to transport the raw material. The marble quarries were located in Makrana, 140 miles west of Agra. Red sandstone was brought from Fatehpur Sikri. A 2.5 mile long ramp was constructed to transport the marble blocks to the top of the building.

Architecturally, the Taj Mahal represents the epitome of the Mughal architecture. It of the marble too reflects the idea of the garden of paradise.

The only thing asymmetrical in the Taj Mahal is Shah Jahan's own crypt. Initially, there was no plan to place his crypt within the building. It is said that he intended to build another Taj Mahal, this one in black marble, on the opposite bank of the river. He then intended to connect them with two bridges, one white, the other black.

A gold and silver railing surrounded the tomb of Mumtaz Mahal. The tomb, in accordance with Muslim tradition, was covered by woven pearls. The doors were made of pure silver with nails of gold. Precious stones imported from all over the world

were inlaid in the white marble. Peter Mundy, an Englishman residing in Agra wrote, 'Gold and silver were used as common metal and marble as ordinary stone.' The illumination came from silver lamps. The air was thick and perfumed with exotic fragrances from silver and gold incense burners. For the maintenance of the Taj, the revenue earned from 31 villages was fixed and a sum of Rs 2,00,000 collected annually.

Eventually, Aurangzeb, Shah Jahan's youngest son, led a rebellion against his father and had his brothers killed. He had the emperor imprisoned in the palace of Agra and had himself crowned emperor of Hindustan.

The Taj Mahal was not the only monument Shah Jahan built. Earlier, he had decided to build himself a brand new city called Shahjahanabad, now known as Old Delhi. That took nine years and cost the treasury six and a half million rupees. For its inauguration, a velvet tent with gold embroidery was erected. It was made with the help of 3,550 workers in a month at the cost of Rs 1,00,000. The emperor floated down the river Jamuna on a barge that resembled a floating palace. On an auspicious time, on April 18, 1648 he entered the Quila Mubarak, the auspicious fort, taking his seat on the famous Peacock Throne.

Peacock Throne: Probably the most expensive throne ever commissioned, the royal treasury issued a thousand kilos of gold for it's making. Eight ft. long, six ft. wide and twelve ft. high, the throne had gold enameling on its sides, its inside entirely covered with rubies, garnets and diamonds. The canopy was supported on twelve columns consisting entirely of emeralds. On top of each column were two peacocks made of sapphires, pearls and diamonds. The fringes of the canopy were decorated with pearls and diamonds. A French jeweller, Tavernier, who visited the royal court, estimated it's cost at Rs 107 million. It took jewellers seven years to make. Shah Jahan himself selected each stone for its beauty, color and lustre. It was a fitting throne for the richest man in the world. (His annual income was Rs 250 million.)

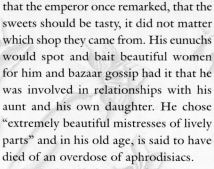

A cross-section of the Taj showing its double dome and an underground chamber where Mumtaz Mahal, and later Shah Jahan, were laid to rest, also a plan of Taj showing the charbagh gardens and water channels (below); Details of the bas-relief work at the Taj (opp page top); and Mughal marble objects d'art — the hookah, incense burner and rose water dispenser (opp page below right)

Shah Jahan mourned his empress for two years and then settled down to a life of considerable promiscuity, though he neither married, nor had other children. It is said,

that the emperor once remarked, that the sweets should be tasty, it did not matter which shop they came from. His eunuchs would spot and bait beautiful women for him and bazaar gossip had it that he was involved in relationships with his aunt and his own daughter. He chose "extremely beautiful mistresses of lively parts" and in his old age, is said to have died of an overdose of aphrodisiacs.

In 1657, Shah Jahan fell ill. Dara Shikhon, his eldest and favorite son, was with him. The other three sons were posted in different parts of the empire - Suja was governor of Bengal, Aurangzeb was governor of the Deccan and Murad was governor of Gujarat.

Although it was public knowledge that Dara Shikhon was the crown prince, a war of succession was inevitable. Since his illness kept Shah Jahan away from the balcony where he appeared daily to receive his people's homage, rumor went around that the emperor was dead and Dara had taken over the throne. Dara had a mystical streak in him. Like his great-grandfather, he was liberal and tolerant. He wrote a book titled 'Merging of the Oceans' accepting all faiths as different rivers culminating in the same ocean. The Muslim clergy were against his liberal views. Aurangzeb used the sentiments of these orthodox Muslims and declared his brother an infidel. He also proved the strongest and shrewdest among the warring brothers. Dara was killed in the battle that broke out among the brothers and his head

was gift wrapped and sent to Shah Jahan. Heart-broken, Shah Jahan wrote to Aurangzeb: 'Do not take good luck for granted.' But Shah Jahan was emperor only in name, for Aurangzeb had usurped that authority, even cutting off the supply of water to his father's palace. He wrote back to his father: 'What you sow, you must reap,' reminding Shah Jahan of his bloody succession.

In the thirty-second year of his accession, Shah Jahan, the fifth emperor among the great Mughals, the builder of the Taj Mahal in Agra and the Red Fort and Jama Masjid in Delhi, was imprisoned in the palace of Agra. Here he lived for another eight years. He was found one morning, sitting on the verandah of Mussam Burj, his eyes gazing at the Taj Mahal across the river, united once more with his beloved empress. His body was bathed, shrouded and taken to the river. Here it was transferred into a boat and taken to his final resting-place, the Taj Mahal. There were no nobles or princes in attendance, only a handful of retainers. Aurangzeb never came to see his father.

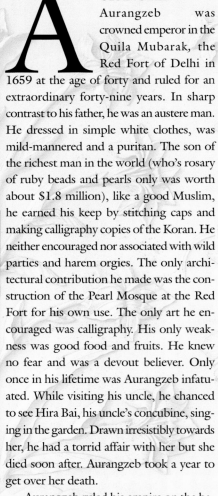

Poitrait of a Mughals, prince embellished with gold *(left)*; Details of the Mughal bas- relief engraving in white marble *(below)*; Bibi ka Maqbara, the tomb of Aurangzeb's wife, in the city of Aurangabad *(opp page)*. Compared to the Taj, the declining architectural standards on Mughal architecture are clearly evident here

AURANGZEB

Aurangzeb was crowned emperor in the Quila Mubarak, the Red Fort of Delhi in 1659 at the age of forty and ruled for an extraordinary forty-nine years. In sharp contrast to his father, he was an austere man. He dressed in simple white clothes, was mild-mannered and a puritan. The son of the richest man in the world (who's rosary of ruby beads and pearls only was worth about $1.8 million), like a good Muslim, he earned his keep by stitching caps and making calligraphy copies of the Koran. He neither encouraged nor associated with wild parties and harem orgies. The only architectural contribution he made was the construction of the Pearl Mosque at the Red Fort for his own use. The only art he encouraged was calligraphy. His only weakness was good food and fruits. He knew no fear and was a devout believer. Only once in his lifetime was Aurangzeb infatuated. While visiting his uncle, he chanced to see Hira Bai, his uncle's concubine, singing in the garden. Drawn irresistibly towards her, he had a torrid affair with her but she died soon after. Aurangzeb took a year to get over her death.

Aurangzeb ruled his empire on the basis of the Shariat, the orthodox Muslim religious law. He forsook the path of religious tolerance his ancestors had adhered to and re-imposed the jizyah (religious tax) on non-Muslims. He stopped the construction of new temples, destroyed important Hindu temples such as Somnath in Gujarat,

Vishwanath in Varanasi and Keshav Rai in Mathura. The broken statues of Hindu gods and goddesses were used as rubble and placed under the steps of the Jama Masjid in Delhi. Cows, holy to Hindus, were butchered inside their temples. He even banned the celebrations of Hindu festivals like Holi and Diwali. Surprisingly, the Rajput rajas remained mute witnesses to

the same battle. The throne of Marwar lay empty. The only hope lay with the two maharanis, both of whom were pregnant. Seeing a power vacuum in Marwar, Aurangzeb seized the occasion to appoint a cousin of the deceased maharaja as heir. The local population was outraged, since they knew the queens were pregnant. Fortunately, a boy was born to one of the

Aurangzeb's oppression. Shivaji, the great Maratha warrior, was the only Hindu king actively opposed to Aurangzeb. Many Rajput rulers were employed in the imperial Mughal army. It was a clever arrangement for the Rajputs, for with neither loss of face nor title, they commanded huge armies for the Mughals.

JODHPUR JUMBLE: In 1678, Jaswant Singh Rathore of Marwar (Jodhpur) was killed while fighting the Afghans on the northwest frontier. His only son died in

queens. The nobles petitioned Aurangzeb to recognize the infant boy as the king. He agreed, but on the condition that the infant be raised as a Muslim. Durgadas, Old Faithful of the royal household, who had led Rajput the delegation to petition, quietly packed off the infant maharaja with a handful of followers, back to Jodhpur. A young boy was dressed as the infant maharaja and female attendants pressed into his service. As feared, the mock maharaja and attendants were

arrested and taken to the Mughal harem. When Aurangzeb was informed that the real maharaja had escaped, he refused to believe it. Reality finally dawned years later when the Marwar prince was betrothed to a princess from Mewar (Udaipur).

While Aurangzeb's rule fostered discontent, in his lifetime he was able to control all dissent. The most noteworthy of these were Jat and Maratha rebellions. Shivaji's guerrilla tactics were a source of great frustration and the Mughal disparaged the Maratha with the epithet 'mountain rat'. Though Aurangzeb's empire was the largest of any Mughal, it also appeared that it lay in wait for his death. He was eighty-nine when he died, outliving his brothers and sisters and some of his children and grandchildren as well. He had left behind instructions that the money earned from the caps he had made be used for his last rites. In stark contrast to his forefathers, he had no tomb built for himself. He lies buried in a small, sleepy village on the way to the Ellora caves near Aurangabad. Only a few Muslim pilgrims come to pray at his grave, which is open to the sky and covered only by grass. The last of the great Mughals, Aurangzeb ruled India with a fanatical zeal.

He realized in his last days that he had sowed the seeds of discontent and wrote: "I came alone and I go as a stranger. I do not know who I am Or what I came for. The instance which has passed in power Has only left sorrow behind. After me, I see only chaos".

END OF EMPIRE
With Aurangzeb's death, the Mughal empire went into decline. There were bloody battles at each succession. Aurangzeb's son, Muazzam, lasted for only five years. Debauched kings followed, unable to hold off the invaders. Somehow, Mohammad Shah Rangeela

(The Colourful) survived for thirty years. When Nadir Shah the Persian came to loot Delhi, he was received at the gates of the fort of Delhi and made to sit on the throne by the emperor himself. Nadir Shah ransacked Delhi and stripped the palaces of their gold and silver.

On his return to Persia, he carried with him the Peacock Throne. So loaded was his caravan with loot that the elephants and camels carrying the booty could only walk four kilometers a day.

The power of the Mughals, who once controlled the length and breadth of India, was now reduced to the confines of the walls of the Red Fort. Outside the walls, the British were the new conquerors. The last Mughal emperor to rule India was Bahadur Shah Zafar. He was made the symbolic head of the rebellion against the British in 1857. It was the last flicker of the dying lamp of the empire. The British imprisoned him and exiled him to Rangoon in Burma. He died there, a broken, sad man. A poet, he wrote: *"I have had such ill fate in my life that I could not get two yards of land in my very own empire for my burial"*.

The British had his three sons hanged to death. The mighty Mughal dynasty who ruled Hindustan for nearly three hundred years, finally came to an end ◆

The glory of the Mughal empire, so evident in its jewellry, marble palaces and tombs inlaid with semi precious stones, came to an end with the death of Bahadur Shah Zafar, the last Mughal emperor who was imprisoned and exiled to Burma by the British in 1857. Candles are lit in the memory of Mumtaz Mahal on her tomb at theTaj *(below)*

HINDUISM

Unlike other major religions, Hinduism does not have a founder, nor is there a religious head or book that lays down rules. This has made the religion dynamic with its unique ability to assimilate rather than oppose other faiths and philosophies. The basis of Hinduism rests in recognizing the Brahman or cosmic power —

the supreme soul of the universe. It is self-existent, absolute and eternal. All things emanate from it and all things return to it. Each human being carries within him a part of this eternal soul i.e.

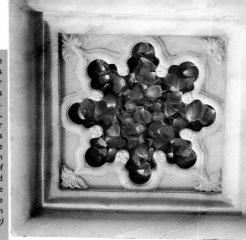

'atman'. The aim of all Hindus is to unite or dissolve their individual soul with the cosmic soul — parmatman.

It is not the parmatman itself that is worshipped but it is the object of abstract meditation that Hindu sages practice in order to attain absorption into it. Since early man was dependent on nature, the elements became the first objects of veneration. The Hindu pantheon, therefore, recognizes their potent force in the guise of Indra (the rain god), Ganga (the river goddess), Chandra (the moon god), Surya (the sun god), Agni (the fire god) and others.

Anything that had a vital influence on one's life was an object of veneration. But as civilization developed and progressed, the gods started assuming human forms.

But at the heart of Hindu philosophy is one omnipresent cosmic power — the Brahman. Since it is difficult to relate to an identity that

does not have a form, the Brahman has been divided into three phases of existence — creation, preservation and destruction (Brahma, Vishnu, Shiva). Every thing in our universe has to pass through these phases, whether a star, microbe or human being. Everything has a beginning and an end. This is a universal law and nothing can change it. The Hindus recognize Brahma as the god of creation, Vishnu as the god of preservation and Shiva as the god of destruction.

Hindu gods and goddesses are worshiped in various places and forms. Even their vehicles, usually animals and birds, are worshipped as well. The praying rituals and objects are as diverse as the country itself as evident from these pictures from various temples of the country

B
RAHMA – THE DIVINE CREATOR

Brahma is usually depicted with a beard and four arms holding a scepter, a lota or water jug, Vedas books of knowledge and a rosary. . Unlike other Hindu gods, Brahma does not hold any weapons in his hands. His consort is Saraswati, the goddess of learning for creation would be impossible without right knowledge. His vehicle is the swan. Brahma, it is

An idol of the four-headed Brahma at the Somnathpur, Mysore *(far left);* Wall painting in the interior of Brahma Temple in Pushkar *(left);* the entrance to Brahma's temple in Pushkar, Rajasthan *(below left);* Brahma riding swans, depicted in the cave temples of Elephanta island near Bombay *(below);* Brahma's consort Saraswati is goddess of learning *(bottom)*

said, created himself by first creating water. In this, he deposited a seed that later became a golden egg. From this egg, Brahma, creator of all worlds, was born. The remaining material of this golden egg expanded into Brahman or the universe. Brahma Purana explains why Brahma has four heads: when Brahma was creating universe he made an exotically beautiful maiden known as Satarupa He was besotted by her beauty. Satarupa moved in various directions to avoid Brahma's longing

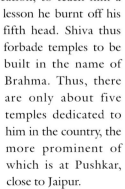

looks but Brahma developed a head in each direction she moved in order not to loose her sight. Consequently he created five heads for himself Shiva, who was witness to entire episode, thought it was unbecoming of Brahma to be besotted by his own creation, to teach him a lesson he burnt off his fifth head. Shiva thus forbade temples to be built in the name of Brahma. Thus, there are only about five temples dedicated to him in the country, the more prominent of which is at Pushkar, close to Jaipur.

VISHNU – THE PRESERVER

In contrast with Brahma, Vishnu has countless temples dedicated to him. He, too, has four arms but holds a conch shell or a discus as attributes. Narayan is another name for Vishnu - 'nara' represents the waters where he resides on the bed of a hundred-headed cobra Anantha or Sesha. The cobra represents cosmic energy, while water represents eternal bliss. The discus or chakra represents dharma or righteousness while the conch-shell or 'shankh' stands for the cosmic sound Om. The mace or 'g a d a' stands for the removal of evil and the lotus, on which Vishnu sits, is a symbol of beauty and purity.

His consort is Lakshmi, the goddess of wealth, for without wealth, preservation would be impossible. Vishnu's vehicle is Garuda, the

Vishnu astride a seven-headed serpent at Somnathpur temple *(above);* a rare painting from Orissa showing all the nine incarnations of Vishnu *(right);* a mural in Samode Palace showing Vishnu's incarnations *(above right);* and two versions of Vishnu's consort Laxmi at the entrances of Indian homes *(opp page)*

mythological half-bird, half-man. Over the ages, he has appeared in nine avatars or incarnations.

MATSAYA, THE FISH

Vishnu in his fish avatar saves Manu, the progenitor of the human race, from catastrophic floods that threatened to drown the whole world. As the story, reminiscent of the Biblical story of Noah and the Ark (but much older than it) goes, Manu came across a tiny fish and undertook its care. In no time, the fish grew to such an immense size that only the ocean could hold it. Manu recognized its divine power and prayed to the fish.

Vishnu now appeared before Manu and fore told him of the catastrophe. When the floods came Manu, along with the holy men and all the seeds of all living beings, boarded a ship he had especially prepared for the task. Vishnu then appeared in the ocean as a giant fish and anchored the ship to a safe place till the waters receded.

KUMRA, THE TORTOISE

Vishnu next appears as a tortoise to recover the things that were lost in the floods by Manu. His back is used as a pivot at the bottom of the sea on which the mountain Mandara is placed and the sea is churned to look for things that lie at the bottom of the ocean. Among the riches that are recovered are 'Amrit' (life-giving water), Dhanvantri (physician of the gods and the holder of Amrit), Lakshmi (goddess of wealth), Sura (goddess of wine), Chandra (moon), Rambha (a nymph) and Surabhi (the cow of plenty).

VARAHA, THE BOAR

In his boar incarnation, Vishnu salvages Prithvi (the Earth) from the clutches of the demon Hiranyakashyap who had dragged it to the bottom of the ocean. Vishnu dives to the bottom of the ocean and after a long battle, raises the Earth to safety.

NARASIMHA, HALF-MAN, HALF-LION

The demon Hiranyakashyap was granted the boon that neither man nor beast could slay him, he could not be killed on heaven or earth and neither during the day nor night. Such immense power soon became too potent for him to handle and he began a reign of terror, troubling both mankind and the gods in heaven. When his son opposed him, the demon seized him and said no one could come to his rescue because he was omnipotent. At this Vishnu, in his half-man-half-lion avatar, burst forth from a pillar in the palace of the demon. He raised the demon on his thigh (so he was neither in heaven nor on Earth) and choosing dusk when it was neither day nor night, finally rid the world of the scourge.

7th century versions of Vishnu saving Prithvi, the earth goddess, at Ellora *(opp below)*; Vishnu kills the demon Hiranyakashipu *(above)*; Vishnu as Vamana measuring the earth and sky, Osian *(right)*; Vishnu's consort Laxmi *(opp page center)*; a 9th Century Chola bronze of Vishnu *(opp page far left)*; Matsaya avtar *(opp page top)*

VAMANA, THE DWARF

King Bali underwent penance and became so powerful as a result of the boons granted to him that he unleashed terror upon everyone. Finally, Vishnu appeared before him as a dwarf and requested him for a small piece of land. Seeing the size of the dwarf, Bali granted him the ownership of three steps of land. Vishnu now grew to a gigantic size, so large that one step covered the Earth, the second Heaven and with his third step, he pushed Bali into hell, the only place left for the demon to escape to.

PARSHURAMA, THE AXE-BEARING RAM

Parshurama was the fifth son of the Brahmin Jamadagni and his consort Renuka. Kartavirya, a Kshatriya king, had a thousand arms and was invincible. One day the Kshatriya

Of the nine incarnations of Vishnu, the most popular ones are Rama, the hero of the epic Ramayana, and Krishna. Rama is always depicted with the bow and arrow *(right);* a painting in Orchha palace depicting the court scene of Rama in Ayodhya *(top)*

king came to the Jamadagni's hut and stole his holy calf. This made Parshurama so angry that he killed the thousand-armed king. In retaliation, Kartavirya's sons killed Parshurama's father. This infuriated Parshurama who wielded his deadly axe to kill all the Kshatriya caste twenty-one times over, filling the lakes with their blood. He then gifted the earth to the great sage, Kashyapa.

and husband. Exiled to the forests for fourteen years on the instructions of his stepmother, his wife Sita was abducted by Ravana, the demon king of Lanka. Rama and his brother Laxman and an army of monkeys led by Hanuman, set out to wage war on Ravana, destroying his glittering city and ridding the earth of evil. It is this tale that is recorded in the great epic, the Ramayana.

RAMA OR RAMCHANDRA

Rama, the eldest son of Raja Dasharatha of Ayodhya, is the role model for all Indian men. The ideal king, he was also the ideal brother, son

KRISHNA

The eighth incarnation of Vishnu holds a popular place in the hearts of millions of Hindus. His

pranks as a child, his love affairs with the gopis — the cow maids of Vrindavan — and other tales are told and re-told in literature, art, music and dance. His discourse to the eldest of the five Pandava brothers on the battlefield in Kurukshetra (with the 100 Kaurava cousins waiting to go to war against them) form the subject for the divine song, the Bhagwad Gita, that forms part of the other great Indian epic, the Mahabharata. Krishna, as a young lad, had killed the demon Kansa and the king of the snakes, Kaliya, who inhabited the waters of the Jamuna.

The 8th incarnation of Vishnu, Krishna, and his consort Radha, figure prominently in the works of Indian artists, they are theme of many paintings in the palaces and havelis *(top)* and dance dramas across the country; A 15th century sculpture of Krishna playing the flute, Somnathpur *(left)*

BUDDHA

Accepted as the last incarnation of Vishnu, scholars now feel this may merely reflect a move by the Brahmins to retain Hindu followers influenced by Buddhism within their fold. Since Buddha himself was born into a Hindu family, this would have been acceptable to most Hindus since the Buddha started out as a Guru. It was only after Buddhism became popular that the Hindu priests began to take notice of the inroads it was making into Hinduism. They may then have simply incorporated the Buddha into their own pantheon of gods.

Buddha is considered the ninth incarnation of Vishnu by Hindus. Fifth century frescoes of Buddha from Ajanta caves temples (above); Buddhist prayer wheels (right); sculpture of Buddha from Gandhara region shows the popularity of the religion in the sub continent (right below)

KALKI, THE GOD YET TO COME

The tenth and

according to mythology, the last of Vishnu's incarnations, will come to rid the world of evil during Kaliyug, the age we are currently living in. Vishnu's incarnation will

Sculpture of Vishnu at Somnathpur *(above);* Vishnu sitting on Sesha – the serpent king, Kanchipuram *(right);* Silver coins depicting the consort of Vishnu – Lakshmi, the goddess of wealth *(below);* Temple entrance showing Vishnu and Lakshmi *(below right)*

present himself seated on a horse and restore righteousness before the end of the world itself.

Vishnu's avatars have been the eternal theme of Indian sculptors . The images of the various incarnations can be seen in all the major medieval temples. Khajuraho, which probably is the most visited of the medieval temples, has a great many of them. The most remarkable is the image of the Varaha avtar in front of the Laxmana temple. In the cities, there are numerous temples dedicated to Krishna. Delhi has a beautiful Laxmi Narayan temple dedicated to Vishnu, Lakshmi. It is an interesting introduction to Hindu gods and goddesses.

S HIVA

The third deity in the Hindu trinity, Shiva is characterized by powerful attributes. As Rudra, he is the destroyer. As Shiva, he is the reproductive power that continuously restores what has been destroyed. The symbol of creation is

It is said that among all the Gods in the Hindu pantheon, Shiva is the easiest to please. A 'bahrupia', man of many faces, plays Shiva in a religious procession *(left);* Shiva with his consort Parvati in a roadside shrine *(above);* a silver statue of Parvati being taken out in a procession during the Teej festival in Jaipur *(right)*

eye on his forehead that is usually kept closed — when open, it so potent it can reduce everything to ashes.

The river Ganga is often seen coiled in his tresses. Legend has it that the river goddess had to descend from heaven to save the souls of King Bhagirath's sons, but unless her fall was broken, the world would have been washed away by her powerful currents. Shiva was called upon to perform the task of breaking her fall and the river descended on earth gently.

Shiva is also known as Neelkantha, the blue-necked, because he swallowed on behalf of the gods, the poison churned

A bronze flagstaff with Shiva and Parvati seated on Nandi in the Brihadishvara temple at Tanjore *(top right)*; Shiva and Parvati above a palace door *(top)*; the Nandi facing the Shiva temple in the Nepal Himalaya. *(above)*; 16th century, 5 ft. high, bronze cobra gilded with gold adorns Shiva's temple in Bhaktpur palace, Nepal *(below right)*

represented in the form of the linga or lingam (phallus) while the female organ, the yoni, represents the female energy of Shakti.

Worshipped as Mahayogi, the great ascetic who has mastered abstract meditation, Shiva is usually shown with matted hair, his body smeared with ash. Shiva has a third

out of the ocean. He holds a trident, his vehicle is the bull Nandi and his favorite city is Kashi or Benares. He dwells on Mount Kailash in the Himalayas.

Another popular representation of Shiva is in the form of the cosmic dancer Nataraja.

Nandi, Shiva's vehicle, facing the original Vishwanath temple in Varanasi *(above);* Shiva as the cosmic dancer Nataraja depicted in a Chola bronze *(below);* 11th century Shiva bestowing grace on saint Chandesha, Gangaikundacholapuram *(right);* Shiva in the fearful aspect of Bhairava, the destroyer of evil *(opp page)*

Bronze icons of the dancing Shiva can be seen in various museums in India and in several southern temples. In this image, Shiva is in the 'tribhanga' form (when the sculpture has three different angles). He is surrounded by a circle of fire (representing the continuity of the universe through creation, preservation and destruction).

A 'bahrupia' dressed as Shiva *(opp page, far left)*; Shiva as Nataraja *(opp page, top left)*; the gods try to see the beginning and end of Shiva's lingam *(opp page, left)*; a Brahmin priest in front of a Shivalingam temple *(above)*; two statues of Shiva built a 1300 years apart *(top right)*; Shiva under a tree *(below)*; A Chola bronze depicting both male and female aspects of Shiva *(right)*

The face of the woman in his matted hair is Goddess Ganga (representing eternity and purity). He wears the moon on his forehead (its waxing and waning denoting time). His right hand raised towards the worshipper denotes protection. The cobras coiled around his neck are a symbol of cosmic energy. The third eye on his forehead denotes his destructive power. A demon under the foot represents the ego that one must suppress. Shiva as Ardhanarishwara (half-man half woman), he represents the inseparability of matter and energy. His vehicle, the Nandi bull, is a symbol of the steadfastness of his followers.

GANESHA

Ganesha is the most popular of Hindu gods. Born to Shiva and Parvati, his elephant-head is easily recognizable. An interesting tale narrates why this pot-bellied god has the head of a pachyderm. Shiva, after his marriage to Parvati, went off to Mount Kailash to meditate. He became so engrossed in his meditation that years went by, during which time Ganesha was born to Parvati. When on completing his meditations, Shiva returned home, he found a young boy posted outside his house, guarding its entrance, refusing to let anybody in because his mother Parvati was bathing inside. Shiva did not know that he was the father of a child and Ganesha, who had never seen him, failed to recognize his father. In a rage, therefore, Shiva cut off the boy's head. A hysterical Parvati insisted that Shiva return her son back to her. Left with no choice, Shiva took Ganesha's body to

Brahma, the lord of creation, who told him to place the boy's head once more upon his neck to restore him to life. But the head had rolled away and was lost. A compromise was sought: Shiva was to kill the first living being he came across

and place it upon his young son's shoulders. Since this was a baby elephant, Ganesha has ever since had an elephant's head. Parvati was unhappy that her son would be ridiculed, but Shiva consoled her saying that Ganesha would be always be worshipped first by people before any other god.

Ganesha's statues, paintings or sculptures decorate Hindu homes, shops and palaces. The elephant-headed deity is revered as the god of good luck who removes all obstacles in everyone's life. On Wednesdays, temples dedicated to Ganesha are full with devotees seeking favours from the generous god. Ganesha idol with his vehical a mouse in front

Which is why Ganesha, the harbinger of good fortune, is invoked first at any ritual or ceremony. Whether it is Diwali puja, a new bullock cart or car, or students pray-

ing before the start of their exams, it is Ganesha who comes to their aid.

Several tales explain why one of his tusks is broken.  Once, when walking to a neighboring village, Ganesha found the journey tiring and sat down to rest. As the evening set in, Chandra the moon rose in the sky and, on spotting Ganesha, he started to make fun of him. Looking for something to throw at it, Ganesha found nothing, so he broke off his tusk and threw it at Chandra. Ever since, the moon god has worn the scars on his face and Ganesha has had a broken tusk. In another story, Ganesha broke off his tusk to use as a pen while writing the Mahabharata being dictated by Sage

Vyasa, for the pen with which he was writing broke and according to the terms established, the Mahabharata had to be written without a pause.

Yet another legend from the Puranas talks about the time Parashurama came to pay his respects to Shiva, but was stopped by Ganesha, who did not want his sleeping father disturbed. In a heated moment, Ganesha grabbed Parashurama by his trunk and threw him to the ground. Parashurama was so enraged that he threw his most powerful weapon, the axe, at Ganesha. Since Ganesha knew the weapon was a gift from his father, he humbly received the blow on his tusk. This led Ganesha to be known as Eka-danta, him of

the single tusk.

Ganesha's chubby body represents the universe. The curled trunk represents the cosmic sound 'Om'. The elephant's head symbolizes intelligence. His big ears enable him to listen easily to his worshippers. The snake around his waist represents cosmic energy. His vehicle is the rat. In the fort at Ranthambore in Rajasthan, there is a temple dedicated to Ganesha where his devotees send wedding invitations and letters that are read aloud to seek his blessings.

The entrance to most Hindu temples is adorned by an idol of Ganesha. In religious rituals the first god to be invoked is Ganesha regardless of the deity whom the ceremony is dedicated to. During the Diwali festival, all Hindus buy new statues of Ganesha which becomes the object of veneration for the rest of the year. Ganesha's favourite sweets that are used as offerings (above)

H

ANUMAN
Hanuman, son of Pavan, the wind god and Kesari, daughter of a monkey king, is known for his strength and his ability to fly. Hanuman teamed up with Rama in his battle against the demon king Ravana, single-handedly

Hanuman is worshipped for his devotion to Lord Rama. Along with the Vanar Sena, or monkey brigade, he plays a key role in Rama's victory over the demon king Ravana. In many pictures he can be seen carrying a Himalayan mountain. Because of Hanuman, monkeys are also considered sacred by Hindus.

scorching his golden city, Lanka. In the same war, when Rama's brother Laxman was wounded, Hanuman was dispatched to fly to the Himalayas to bring back an herb that would cure him. Unable to recognize the plant, Hanuman uprooted an entire mountain and carried it back, so that the antidote could be found and used for the cure. Also called Maruti or Marutputra in the ancient scriptures, Hanuman was well versed in grammar and considered the ninth author of grammar. His physical strength has ensured that he is the lord of the akharas or gymnasiums.

There are numerous shrines dedicated to him and Tuesday is considered auspicious for worshipping him. Idols and often, just stones daubed with red or orange are used to depict him. Images show him holding up the Himalayas in one hand as he flies through the skies, or tearing open his chest to reveal his beloved Rama and Sita dwelling in his heart.

A lady praying at a roadside Hanuman shrine *(left)*. Hanuman is also the divine patron of akharas, or local gyms, where Indian style wrestling is the prized sport. The wrestlers idolize Hanuman for his immense power and celibacy. The auspicious day to pray to Hanuman is Tuesday as any visit to a temple dedicated to this god would testify

S SHAKTI,
COSMIC ENERGY
In Hindu philosophy, while gods represents matter, goddesses are a symbol of energy. Of the two energies that make the universe – dynamic and static – the god-

desses represent the dynamic nature of the cosmos. Since matter and energy are complementary, Brahma, the god of creation, has

Devi is the manifestation of the divine energy. She is revered to by the Tantriks and the warriors alike. She rides a tiger, has ten arms, each adorned with a weapon, thus denoting the destructive power of the goddess in the wall painting at Samode palace near Jaipur *(above);* As goddess Durga she is the destroyer of demon Mahisasur, the one with a buffalo head, Mandore *(left);*

Devi, or Mother Goddess, has various names, attributes and forms such as, Shakti, or female energy. In her normal form she is known as Uma. In her fierce aspect she is revered as Durga, Chamundi and Bhairavi. In her most fearful form she is Kali, the goddess who wears a garland of the skulls of the evil men she has killed to save the world

Saraswati, the goddess of knowledge, as his consort. Without knowledge, creation is impossible. Vishnu, the god of preservation, has Lakshmi, the goddess of wealth, as his spouse. Shiva, the lord of destruction, has Parvati, the cosmic energy that is needed for destruction, as his wife. This manifestation of divine energy is represented in many forms - as Durga she kills the demon Mahisasur and fights the eight evils; as the dark Kali, she is the

personification of time. There is an interesting legend in the Puranas on the creation of divine energy. Brahma, so goes the tale, goes to consult Shiva about an asura or demon named Andhka who has become a menace to all the devtas or gods. The two gods summon Vishnu and using their divine energies, create a beautiful woman who's body represents the past, present and future through the colors black, white and red. The beautiful maiden then divided herself into three parts - the white becoming Saraswati who helped Brahma create the universe; the red became Lakshmi who helped Vishnu preserve the universe; and the black becoming Parvati blessed with the energy of Shiva ◆

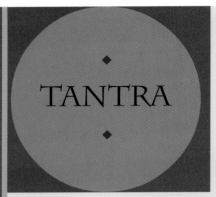

TANTRA

Hindu Tantra has been developed as a mystical, but very detailed path to ecstatic release, which harnesses the infinite energies of mind and body. It is yoga of action, not abstract contemplation.

5th and 8th centuries AD. These cover a wide range of subjects from astrology to history and theology and most are presented as dialogues between Shiva, usually acting as the guru (teacher) and Shakti, his consort and pupil. The Tantra movement was at its peak by the 10th century AD. Temples were built throughout northern India to the 64 'yoginis' (Tantrik goddesses). In the golden age of Indian art, Tantrik masons sculpted the remarkable erotic friezes at Khajuraho and Konarak.

There were two major strands of Tantra - the Left-hand ('vama-marg') and Right-hand ('dakshina-marg') paths. While the

Rather than deny themselves the fruits of worldly pleasures, Tantriks (practitioners of Tantra) strive to gain the fullest possible pleasure from them. The experience or realization of their enjoyment reaches such high levels that the energy unleashed can carry consciousness to the peak of enlightenment.

The word tantra, means "extension" of the mind. It refers to 64 Tantras (religious texts) composed between the

The union of male and female energies - Shiva and Shakti - in a wall painting at Jodhpur Fort *(above);* a 18th Century silver tantrik figure *(right);* and paintings showing different centers of energies in a human body *(above right and opp page)*

Right-hand way was practiced by Tantra's more conservative followers, who concentrated on interpreting the texts intellectually, the Left-hand path was marked by esoteric rituals and body magic, especially the use of sexual intercourse.

Tantriks usually rejected the notion of a remote, transcendent deity, known only through contemplation. Instead, they honored the 'shakti' (manifest power) of godhead, incarnate in the form of Shakti, the goddess. This led them to believe that women were the holders of divine power. The union of male and female, transcendent and immanent godhead was symbolized by ritual

sexual intercourse.

Tantra, associates physical sexual energy, with the drive for resolution of opposites and visualized the human body itself as a plant whose roots feed

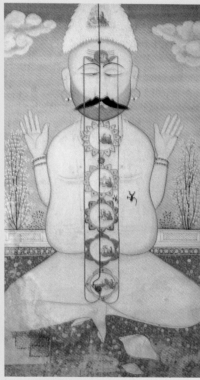

on the pure energy of undiluted godhead. Like the sap of a plant, this energy was thought to flow through a network of veins that Tantriks believed to be the 'subtle body' formed about the axis of the spinal column.

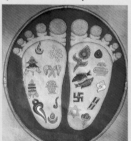

Tantriks were ritually initiated into their sects during sexual intercourse with a female power holder. Sexual intercourse was believed to replicate the process of creation, whereby the "red energy" of the 'yoni' (vulva), is continuously fertilized by the "white energy" of the seed ◆

KARMA

Hindus believe in reincarnation. They give credence to an after-life and are convinced that how they fare in it will be based on the deeds of their present life. The deeds or actions of a previous life are known as karma. One's present life is nothing more than the reflection of one's deeds in a previous life. This is similar to the sowing of crop – the kind of seeds sown ensures the quality of the crop in the coming season.

Death, to the Hindu, is not dissimi-lar to changing one's clothes, for it is in a similar manner that a soul changes a body upon its death. The goal of each Hindu is to ensure that the individual

Karma is the reflection of our deeds of the past life as manifest in the present one. A man constantly tries to improve his Karma by following the faith and good deeds. The ultimate goal is to elevate oneself from the cycle of birth and rebirth and reach the state of eternal happiness known as Moksha

soul or atman should unite with the cosmic soul or parmatman.

Another important incident in Indian mythology is narrated in the Mahabharata. On the eve of the great battle, Arjuna, the bravest of the five Pandava brothers, is ambivalent about the need to fight, for standing on the other side are his own cousins. Lord Krishna is in the battlefield as Arjuna's charioteer and gives him a discourse, now well known as the Bhagwad Gita. The essence of the discourse, familiar to all Indians, is that karma begets dharma: or that your good deed is your religion.

There is profound belief in destiny: that, which is to happen, will. This should not be mistaken for either laziness or fatalism, for if their previous life has cast its shadow on the present, then how you react to it will have a bearing on your next life.

Hindus believe that in this cycle of births and rebirths, it takes 52 million births to be born as a human. Once acquired, it should not be frittered away with

bad karma, for that would result in back-
ward incarnations: such as being reborn
as a leper, for instance, or as an animal.
Our human life offers us the opportunity to elevate ourselves from the cycle
of birth and rebirth. This state is known
as nirvana or moksha.

To achieve this eternal truth is difficult, as the world's illusory materialism
often leads one to deviate from the
knowledge of real truth. This illusion is
maya: a world where
wealth, property, egoism,
jealousy and relationships

create temptations. Hinduism believes that nothing in this world is permanent. Just as the lotus flower elevates itself from the stagnant water surrounding it, so also one should elevate oneself from the worldly desires of maya. The recognition of this desire and the fight to stave it off, forms the basis of eastern philosophies such as Hinduism, Jainism and Buddhism.

This may denote the absence of stress from the Indian way of life. After all, if there is anything left incomplete in this birth, the next birth will offer the opportunity of completing the task. This is something Western religions and philosophies do not dwell upon ◆

You reap what you sow is the essence of the law of Karma. One's Karma is to do the job well and not worry about profit, says the Bhagwat Gita. The Sati hands on the left and cremations on the river banks depict the end of the journey which is aiming for Moksha, or liberation from an earthly existence

YOGA

Yoga in ancient Sanskrit language means to unite or to join, literally it implies the union of mind and body. It is a practical path to self-realization, a means of attaining enlightenment by purifying the entire being, so that the mind-body can experience the absolute reality underlying the illusions of everyday life. It is one of the most famous of Hinduism's philosophical traditions, now practiced people all over the world. Yoga is less a religion than a mode of spiritual progress, in which bodily discipline influences consciousness and concentrating the mind gives the adept mastery over matter. Simple exercises are said to lend the adept yogic powers such as levitation, for which yoga is renowned.

Advanced yogis claim to possess extraordinary powers, such as the ability to control their own metabolism and in extreme samadhis even the heartbeat is controlled. Whereas Raja Yoga rejects the body as an illusion, Hatha Yoga uses it as a method of liberation. Hatha yogis practice to discipline and purify the body so that they can construct a new subtle body that is immune to 'karma' and disease. Once purified, the subtle body-mind attains the ecstatic state of 'samadhi' and intensive meditation then leads to its release. Kundalini yoga seeks the union of Shiva and Shakti within the yogi's body by drawing the 'serpent' of immanent female power up to the energy center at the top of the head, the location of transcendent godhead.

The earliest historical depiction of Yoga is from a five thousand years old seal found during the excavations of Indus valley Civilization. It depicts a yogi sitting cross-legged in a meditative pose, it is generally attributed to Shiva in his form as Pashupati. The first written reference of yoga is in Rig Veda, which was supposedly written some 3500 years ago. Then about two thousand years ago, sage Patanjali compiled 196 aphorisms known as Yoga sutras of Pathanjali, which is a form of Raja yoga or the path of meditation towards the enlightenment. Ashtanga

yoga or Eight Limbs school of Patanjali yoga are (1) Yama – abstentions from violence, deceit, theft, illicit sex and possession. (2) Niyama – to observe purity, contentment, austerities, learn and surrender to almighty. (3) Asana - Meditative position – today, the term asanas are usually used for yogic positions. (4) Parnayama – control of life giving force though regulation of breathing. (5) Pratyahara – here the consciousness of the individual is internalized in order that the sensations from the senses of taste, touch, sight, hearing and smell don't reach their respective centers in the brain. With this, the Sadhaka, or disciple, is free to meditate without distractions. (6) Dharana - is concentration where the object being meditated upon is held in the mind without consciousness wavering from it. (7) Dhyana – in this state, the consciousness of the act of meditation disappears, and only the consciousness of being and the object of concentration exist. (8) Samadhi – Liberation, here n the final stage of Samadhi, the self also dissolves, and the meditator becomes one with the object.

Hatha yoga Pradipika was compiled by sage Yogi Swatmarama, in 15th century. In this treatise Swatmarama describes Hatha Yoga as 'a stairway that leads to Raja Yoga'. It is a preparatory stage of physical purification called shatkarmat that renders the body fit for higher meditation. The word Hatha is a compound of the words Ha and Tha meaning sun and moon and refers to the principal nadis (energy channels) of the subtle body that must be fully operational to attain a state of dhyana or samadhi. Hatha Yoga and its numerous modern interpretations are what most westerners associate the word yoga with. In the west it is mostly practiced for its physical attributes.

Yogic exercises have positive effect on the human body. Yoga is known to reverse heart conditions, help in controlling diabetes and blood pressure. Its practice gives you clarity of thought and controles emotions such as anger, greed and ego ◆

Yoga is an ancient Indian science which helps achieve the union of mind and matter through physical training of the body in various postures known as asanas. The basic and most common and effective is Padmasana, or the lotus position *(above)*

SADHUS
INDIAN ASCETICS

The theme that the material world is an illusion or 'maya', is echoed repeatedly in Hindu, Buddhist and Jain philosophy. In the Hindu tradition, 'sadhus' are ascetics who follow a path of penance and austerity to attain enlightenment. Believing the world to be made by the creative force of 'maya', sadhus are renunciants, rejecting worldly attachments and a life of action, as it were, to erase past actions and so liberate themselves into the world of divine reality.

Many sadhus imitate the mythological life of Shiva, the greatest of all ascetics. They carry a symbolic trident and wear three stripes of ash upon their foreheads to represent Shiva's triple aspect and his ascetic quest to destroy three impurities — selfishness, action with desire and maya.

An ascetic devotee of Shiva, known as a sadhu, uses sandalwood paste to put the holy sign on his forehead *(above);* another sadhu meditates at dawn *(left);* a sadhu with his disciples in east India *(opp top);* a baharupia dressed as Shiva *(opp center);* and a sadhu with a python around his neck *(opp bottom)*

The saffron-colored robes worn by sadhus signify the fertile blood of Parvati, Shiva's consort. They are a common sight on the country's roads and survive on 'bhiksha' or donations, in exchange for which they explain the

philosophy of life in a layman's language. Among the sadhus, the Nagas are the most prominent since they remain naked, covered only by 'vibhuti' or sacred ash. They let their hair grow in dreadlocks called 'jata'. The sadhus are divided into three main 'akharas' or denominations, founded in the 8th century by Adi Shankaracharya, the great sage. He established four 'maths' or centres in the four cardinal extremes of India.

In these akharas, sadhus are taught to control mind and body and become masters in yoga.

The markings on their foreheads not only describe the sect they belong to, but also each sub-sect. Whenever sadhus visit cities or villages, each householder, according to his economic capability, voluntarily offers them food, money and clothing. Most do their own cooking. With the exception of religious gatherings like the Kumbha Mela and Pushkar Mela where they spend months, sadhus rarely stay at one place, spending the nights at an ashram, temple or cremation ground.

The initiation ceremony to

the monastic order contains the last rites of death which a novice must perform himself. This symbolizes his breaking away from the past and entering a new life. This is the reason why a sadhu is not cremated after his death but is either buried or put to rest in water (jal samadhi).

Sadhus usually spend the first years of renunciation with their gurus. Traditionally sadhus shave their heads as a sign of renunciation. Once fully acquainted with the spiritual and yogic arts, they leave their guru's protection to wander the roads and forests, never staying long in one place for they believe that moving around keeps the body-mind alert and staying in one place leads to stagnation.

The life of a sadhu is one of penance and austerity to gain enlightenment. Sadhus consider the world an illusion, or maya. They cover their bodies with ash to remind them of the end. Their hair, which is allowed to grow for years, is called jata and the alms bowl is known as kamandal

The largest number of sadhus belong to the Juna Akhara, famous for

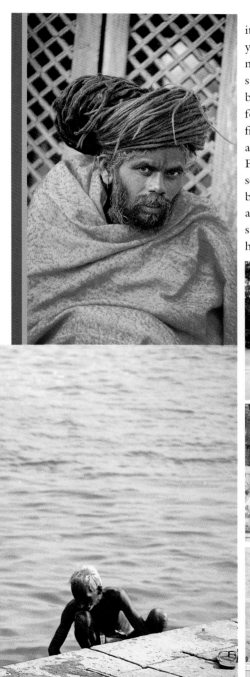

its extremity of its penance and the yogic accomplishments of its members. Many members of the sect perform penances such as burying their heads in the ground for days at a time to attract alms from passers-by. Hindus hold sadhus and sanyasis in high esteem. From politicians to businessmen, scientists and professionals, everyone bows down to touch their feet and seek their blessings, for a true sadhu has powers bestowed on him by the divinity ◆

KUMBHA MELA

The churning of the oceans from which the of sacred water pot, or Kumbh, emerges *(left)*; millions take a dip in the Ganges on the occasion of the great Kumbh *(opp page bottom)*; an image of the goddess Ganges astride a crocodile *(opp page center)*

Makar Sankranti, the new moon day when Jupiter is in Aquarius (kumbh or pot in India) and both the Sun and Moon are in Capricorn.

Prayag marks the sangam or confluence of three rivers — the Jamuna, Ganga and Saraswati, the last a mythical river. Bathing in the festival is significant for one can wash away accumulated bad karma of one's life and get liberation from samsara.

The Kumbha festival lasts for three months. During this period, millions of devotees (on the last count 35 million) come to bathe in the holy waters of the confluence of the Ganga and Jamuna. One of the principal features is the holy dip undertaken by the sadhus.

The most spectacular of these sights is

The Kumbha Mela is the largest congregation of humanity on earth. The word kumbha stands for the pot that contains the nectar of immortality, which, according to Hindu mythology, came from the churning of the ocean. The gods and demons fought for its possession and in the struggle, a few drops from the pitcher fell on four places on earth. These have since become sacred sites for the Kumbha Mela.

Mela is held every twelve years (coinciding with one round of Jupiter through the zodiac) among four locations: Allahabad (Paryag), Haridwar, Ujjain and Nasik. At Prayag, the *Kumbh Mela* is held in the month of Magh (January/February). The most auspicious day for bathing is

the procession of 'shahi snan' or royal bath of the Naga sadhus. They march naked in the freezing cold of north India with their bodies covered in holy ash, matted locks of hair flowing down to their waist, and their tridents (the symbol of Lord Shiva) raised high, they enter the holy waters of Ganga, blowing conch shells and shouthing "Ganga ki jai," (hail goddess Ganges).

The head of each math or order leads the procession with thousands of followers singing praises of the Almighty. They carry embroidered umbrellas, silver staffs, garlands, trumpets, drums etc. Some are seated on elephants, others on horses, while millions simply walk. The areas for bathing are demarcated and timings fixed. Prayers are read, offerings of fruits, flowers and sweets made to the river after which the sadhus take their holy dip ◆

According to Hinduism, there are four stages or ashrams to a man's life and he must adhere to these for an ordered existence.

BRAHMACHARYA

The first stage of existence begins with the thread ceremony called Upanayanam, during which ceremony, the child is considered to be born again. The three strands of the sacred thread remind the student of God, intelligence and respect for the guru. After the ceremony the child is dispatched to live on his own at a guru's hermitage. Here the guru enlightens young minds with yoga, the scriptures, discipline and dharma.

GRIHASTHA ASHRAM

In the second phase of a man's life, as householder, he settles down in a married life, he earns his money through honest means, reserving a tenth of it for charity. In this phase of his life, he enjoys sensual pleasures, brings up his children with proper education and arranges their marriages.

VANAPRASTHA ASHRAM

Once his social obligations are over, the children married and settled, the

householder starts to disassociate himself from worldly pleasures in the pursuit of eternal truth. He now prepares to lead a simple existence in the jungle.

SANYAS

The last stage of a man's life is a renunciation of all desire.

THE FOUR STAGES OF LIFE

◆

◆

Becoming a recluse, he now spends the major part of his life in hermitages in the foothills of the Himalayas. He spends time practicing yoga to help purify his heart and mind. With the help of pranayama, he slowly lifts the veil that covers his mind, so that he is able to practice dhyana or total concentration that,

The Chattwal family in the Grihasth ashram *(far left)*; Bhramchari students from a gurukul in South India *(below)*; Vanaprastha - a monk walking away from worldly comforts *(above)*; sanyasis who have broken all ties with society and even their families *(left and right)*

in turn, helps control one's senses. Eventually, one enters samadhi, a state when the subject of the meditation and the object become one. This helps one attain moksha or liberation from the cycle of birth and death ◆

UNDERSTANDING THE CASTE SYSTEM

The caste system is unique to Hindu society. Its origin can be traced back to the initial stages of civilization. With the discovery of copper and iron, the nomadic tribes began to sow crops and with it arose the need for settlements. These nascent societies soon evolved manageable forms of local government and administration. They elected an administrator with the title of Raja. The Raja was supported by a council of ministers that were each accountable to local assemblies called Sabha and Samiti.

As trade grew in villages along the Ganga, the people within each society came to be recognized by their principal occupation. Some sociologists feel that the caste system sprang from this division of labor.

In our ancient language Sanskrit, the word for caste is 'varna' which, when translated, means color. The fair-skinned Aryans who had conquered the dark-skinned Dravidians, who were the original occupants of the lands in the north, were at the upper end of this hierarchy. Eventually, therefore, the four-fold division of society came to be tied in with the color of a person's skin.

Brahmins: Tall and fair-skinned, with sharp features, they were accorded the duties of the priest and teacher.

Kshatriyas: The warrior caste bore the responsibility of maintaining law and order within the community and provided protection against invaders.

Vaishyas: The traders were of relatively darker skin and were also assigned menial tasks.

Shudras: As the social structure grew increasingly complex, a fourth class was gradually added to the list. The Shudras performed cleaning and sanitation work; and they removed and skinned dead animals. They lived on the outskirts of society, often on the boundaries of the village.

Initially, the caste system was fluid, enabling movement from one level to another, until an increasingly complicated social administration set out to curb this flexibility by decreeing that birth and death alone would determine one's caste.

The Brahmins, to safeguard their societal privileges, provided intellectual justification for the caste system in quoting from the Vedas. According to these Hindu scriptures, when

Brahma created the human being, he also created the caste system. From the mouth of Brahma came the Brahmins, their job being to preach. From his arms came the

Kshatriyas, their task the protection of society. From his loins were born the Vaishyas whose job involved business. Finally, from his feet came the Shudras and they carried the weight of all society in performing their menial and filthy work.

By about 600 BC, the caste system was irrevocably fixed, with the Brahmins becoming the key advisors to the government, the Kshatriyas making up the army and Vashiyas managing the trade and manufacture and the Shudras relegated to the fringes of society. The second and the third castes had prospered and they resented the suffocating control of the Brahmins over society. Their salvation lay in the form of two new philosophies that later became world religions – Jainism and Buddhism. The new religions offered equality and increased social mobility among all classes of society.

Caste in modern India: According to the letter of the Indian Constitution, it is illegal to discriminate or distinguish a person on the basis of his or her caste. A Harijan (Gandhi's name for the Shudras meaning, literally, God's people) leader B.R. Ambedkar was one of the key people involved in drafting the Constitution. Today, the politically correct term for Shudra is 'Dalit'.

In metros, in day-to-day life, caste plays an insignificant role. In fact, with evolving lifestyles, it is now disappearing. But the caste system continues to have a strong hold in villages where 80 per cent of India's population still lives. There the caste factor plays an important role at the time of marriages and during elections. The candidates in the villages are elected on the basis of their castes and not on the basis of the election manifestos. However, till date, traditional jobs continue to follow the caste system ◆

The bindi is the mark on the forehead worn by Hindu women. Married women denote their marital status through 'sindoor', vermillion powder dusted in the parting of their hair, or by painting red bindis on

THE BINDI AND THE TILAK

with their sarees. Men can also be seen with markings on their foreheads. These are usually put during a religious ceremony or on a visit to a temple. These are known as 'tilaks'. Such religious marks are put both on male and female foreheads. Symbolically, a tilak connotes the opening of the third eye of inner intelligence. The science of kundalini yoga recognizes centres of energy within the human body called 'chakras'. The first chakra is

Hindu women usually sport a bindi, a cosmetic decoration, on the forehead *(opp page top);* Men, too, adorn their forehead with a mark called the tilak to proclaim their religious belief *(opp page and below);* A vermillion vendor in Varanasi *(opp page bottom)*

their forehead. Widows are not permitted to wear any markings on their forehead. Bindis come in all imaginable shapes and sizes. While, earlier, bindis were painted on the forehead with the use of powders, nowadays for the modern Indian woman, sticker-bindis are more practical. The wide variety of colors help the women to match them

positioned at the base of the spinal cord while the sixth chakra is situated on the forehead, just above the center of the eyebrows and called ajna chakra.

The sadhus and sanyasis wear different tilaks on their foreheads depending on their sect. The tradition of the tilak is centuries old. The coronation ceremony in Indian kingdoms was marked by the Raj Purohit or Chief Priest anointing the forehead with the raj tilak. It is also used to welcome guests and family members home, or bid them good-bye. It is an essential part of religious ceremonies ◆

THE MAHABHARATA

With over 100,000 stanzas, the Mahabharata ('Great Epic of the Bharata Dynasty') is perhaps the longest poem ever composed. It stands, with the Ramayana, as one of the two great Sanskrit epics. Originally titled 'Jaya' (Victory), it was probably begun in the 4th or 3rd Century BC. However many amendments were made and it was not completed until the end of the Gupta dynasty in the 4th Century AD. However, much of the material is far older dating back to the Vedic period. Indeed, some of the stories would have been familiar to audiences as early as 1000 BC. For example, Indra, the Vedic rain god, is mentioned several times in earlier parts of the text although by the 4th century BC he was scarcely a figure from folklore.

Krishna appears in the epic as the leader of his people and an ally of the Pandavas. He still appears more a super-human warrior than a God in his battles alongside the Pandavas, but he grows in

A wall painting depicting Krishna driving Arjuna's chariot in the Mahabharat *(above)*; Krishna on the pillar of a temple in Kanchipuram *(opp page top)*; the cover of the holy text of the Mahabharat *(opp page center)*; Krishna at the entance of Lake Palace, Udaipur *(opp page bottom)*

and think whenever the meaning became unclear. Called the 'Homer of the east', Vyasa is said to have composed the entire Mahabharata and all eighteen Puranas, besides the four books of the Vedas. He was also a priest and a teacher. Vyasa has a vital piece in the narrative. He is the father of some of the principal characters in the epic – the opposed dynasties of the Sons of Darkness and the Sons of Light – and he himself often appears in the story to advise the characters in need or to soothe the distressed.

The central plot of the Mahabharata concerns two dynasties – the Pandavas and Kauravas. The rival families are cousins, the sons of Vyasa's two sons: the blind Dhritrashtra and the pious Pandu.

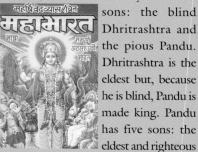

stature to emerge finally as the divine teacher of humanity.

According to legend, the entire Mahabharata was dictated by the sage Vyasa (whose name in Sanskrit means 'Compiler') to the elephant-headed god Ganesha who made one condition: he would only agree to write it down if it was told without a pause. However fast it was dictated, Ganesha kept pace. At one time he broke off a tusk to use in place of a damaged stylus, so as not to break the flow of the sacred words. The denser, more speculative passages, were apparently attempts to slow the deity down, forcing him to stop

Dhritrashtra is the eldest but, because he is blind, Pandu is made king. Pandu has five sons: the eldest and righteous Yudhishthir, Bhim who has great strength, Arjuna the skilled warrior and the twins Nakul and Sahdev. Dhritrashtra, on the other hand, has 100 sons, the eldest of whom is the scheming Duryodhan. When Pandu dies, his blind but well intentioned brother Dhritrashtra takes Pandu's sons

into his own palace. In time Dhritrashtra divides his kingdom, giving half of it to Yudishthir and the other half to Duryodhan. However, Duryodhan becomes jealous of the affection his father feels for his cousin and even more the half of the kingdom that the Pandava's have inherited. Through trickery and cunning, the Pandavas are forced into exile and have to wait thirteen years before they have a chance to reclaim their kingdom.

This is the cause of the epic war that follows, resulting in the destruction of the entire race, except for one survivor who continues the dynasty. This war forms the backdrop of the sacred text of the 'Bhagwad Gita'.

In essence, the Maha-bharata is about the great battle fought in Kurukshetra, where the Pandavas took on the

Kauravas. However, the bravest of the Pandava brothers, Arjuna, is hesitant about waging war against his cousins. At this juncture, Lord Krishna delivers him a lengthy sermon on dharma, the duty as a warrior to fight for righteousness. The essence of this discourse is recorded as the Bhagwad Gita.

Eventually, good triumphs and the Pandava brothers win back their kingdom and the wounded Bhishmapitama, granduncle of both cousins, explains the duties of statecraft and the responsibilities of the ruler to Yudhishthir. The teachings of the Bhagwad Gita are without compare in Hindu philosophy. They underscore one's duty of nishkarma, moral ethics devoid of greed, jealousy and senseless competition ◆

THE RAMAYANA

The Ramayana is the most popular mythological story in India. It is read at home, in temples, as religious discourses and acted out in plays. It is the oldest of the Indian epic poems, written in Sanskrit by the sage Valmiki in, the 5th century BC. It has seven kands or sections and contains 50,000 lines.

The story deals with the seventh incarnation of Lord Vishnu who came to earth to rid it of Ravana, the ten-headed demon king of Lanka. Ravana had prayed before Brahma and observed severe austerities. As a result, Brahma had no choice but to grant him the boon of

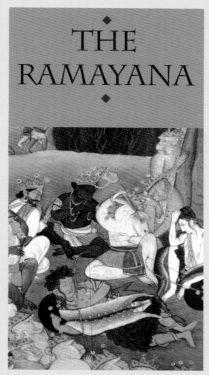

immortality. He could not be killed by either gods or by demons. It didn't take long for Ravana to get intoxicated on his newfound power. He started harassing both gods and mortals alike. The gods were worried by his behavior and decided the only way they could eliminate him was by sending Vishnu to earth in the guise of a mortal being. The powerful Ravana had never thought that a human could be a match for him.

Lord Vishnu came to earth as Rama, the eldest of Raja Dashratha's four boys. His younger brothers were Laxman, Bharat and Shatrughan. Rama married Sita, the

A religious painting showing Hanuman with his army of monkeys and Lord Rama resting with his brother Laxman *(above);* Rama takes aim at the ten-headed demon Ravana *(left);* the occasion which is celebrated as Dussera; a wall painting of Krishna in the Bundi palace *(opp page top)*

beautiful daughter of Raja Janaka, winning her in a competition, which all the princes of the land attended.

After the marriage, Dashratha decided to abdicate and make Rama king of Ayodhya. The announcement was welcomed throughout the kingdom with joy, but Dashratha's second wife reminded the King of a promise made to her and asked that her son Bharat be made king and Rama be exiled to the jungle for fourteen years. The King could not go back on his word and so Rama, accompanied by Sita and his brother Laxman, headed for the jungle. The heartbroken Dashratha died

Laxman settled in a small hut in Chitrakoot, between the rivers Jamuna and Godavari. In the forest they encountered the demon Suparnakha, Ravana's sister, who fell in love with the handsome princes. Rejected by them, she attacked them and Laxman cut off her nose, ears and breasts. An army of demons that came to avenge her honor was trounced by the brothers. When Ravana heard of what had occurred, he too decided to avenge his sister's honor. He had also heard of Sita's beauty. He lured the brothers away from the hut in the guise of a deer and then returned to Sita dressed as a sadhu, begging for food. When Sita

soon after and Bharat, who was crowned king, refused to sit on the throne. He went to the jungle to persuade Rama to return to Ayodhya. Rama, however, refused to return till his exile was over. So, Bharat returned with Rama's sandals, which he placed, on the throne as a mark of respect. Rama, Sita and

came out to give him food, he kidnapped her and took her to Lanka. On the way, the king of vultures, Jatayu engaged him in combat but was fatally wounded. However, before he died, he was able to inform Rama and to save her. Meanwhile, the army of monkeys had managed to build a bridge of stones across the ocean. Rama and his army led the final assault on Lanka. A fierce battle ensued with losses on both sides and though both Rama and

Rama anxiously awaits the arrival of Hanuman with magical herb sanjeevni, the only medicine which can cure his wounded brother Laxman. Hanuman fails to find the herb among the many plants so he uproots the whole mountain and brings it to Rama (above)

Laxman of the kidnapper's identity.

The brothers sought the help of the king of monkeys, Sugriva and his army of monkeys, the vanar sena, led by Hanuman, who could fly. He proved to be of great use to Rama, spying on Ravana's activities in Lanka. He also managed to meet Sita and tell her that Rama was on the way

Laxman suffered injuries, they were able to kill the demons. In the penultimate fight between Ravana and Rama, good triumphed over evil.

Twenty days after his victory over ten headed demon Ravana, Rama returned to Ayodhya to find that houses were illuminated with oil lamps in his honor. To this day, centuries later, Ram's victory over Ravana is celebrated as Dashera festival and twenty days later, Ram's return to Ayodhya is celebrated in the form of Diwali, the festival of lights ◆

BUDDHA THE ENLIGHTENED ONE

Siddharth Gautam was born in Lumbini, in Nepal, close to its border with India, some 2,500 years ago. Gautam's father was the chief of the Sakya clan of warriors. After his birth, the child's mother had a dream about a white elephant. As was common, the court astrologer was called to interpret the dream. The astrologer's finding perturbed the king - the royal child, he said, would one day grow up to be a famous monk. The king wanted his son to be a warrior and ruler, not a monk. The court, therefore, devised a plan to keep the prince confined within the palace, always surrounded by beautiful objects and luxuries. As he grew, it became apparent that the prince wasn't attracted by luxuries, but would devote hours to thinking. His parents arranged his marriage with a beautiful princess and from this union was born a son they named Rahul. One day, while walking as usual in the garden, Gautam saw an old lady who was shrivelled and walked with the help of the stick. Gautam asked his

Fifth century painting form Ajanta caves depicting Buddha's return to his palace as a bhikshu where his son and wife come out in tears to give him alms *(right)*; 23 feet long sculpture of Buddha depicting Parinirvana, or transportation to heaven *(below)*

attendant what was wrong with the old woman. His attendant replied there was nothing wrong with her and that she only

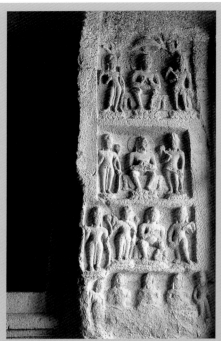

He stayed hungry for so many days that his ribs and veins became visible. Thinking he was a statue of some saint, an untouchable woman offered him milk that Gautam accepted and drank. This horrified his disciples who thought him to be a false tapasvi unable to remain hungry in penance. They

suffered from the rigours of old age. For the first time it struck the young prince that everybody was fated to grow old. Later, on his walks, he saw first a sick man and then the body of a dead man. His uncertainties about the sorrows that the human body had to undergo were cleared when, on another day, he came upon a sadhu, a mystic, holy man whose face shone with knowledge. Gautam now took to wondering what this man had that the others did not. He decided he would not rest till he found the truth. From then on, he wandered from village to village as a bhikshu asking for alms. He sought refuge with gurus, but no one could give him the answers to the mystery of life, or satisfy his thirst for knowledge. Finally, accompanied by five disciples, Gautam decided to meditate on his own.

abandoned Gautam who now sat under a bodhi tree in Bodhgaya and meditated continuously for 45 days. Nothing could distract him for he had attained a state of enlightenment known as moksha. From then on, he was called Buddha, the enlightened one. Buddha now journeyed to Sarnath, near Varanasi, to seek out his five disciplines and there delivered his first sermon before them. He spoke of the four noble truths:

Life is full of suffering.
Suffering is caused by desire.
Suffering can be overcome with control of desire.
To control desire, follow the eight-fold path.

The eight-fold path consists of: *Right aspiration, Right knowledge, Right speech, Right behavior, Right livelihood, Right efforts, Right mindfulness, Right concentration.*

The Buddha's teachings were never written down during his lifetime. They continued to be passed on by word of

A 5th Century column showing the Buddha in various mudras *(opp page far left);* the Buddha in the preaching mudra at the rock cut temples of Ajanta *(centre);* an artist creating a Thanka painting depicting the life of the Buddha *(left);* and Buddhist prayer wheels *(bottom)*

people, he had pillars (known as the Ashoka pillars) inscribed with his teachings all over his kingdom. His son carried a sapling of the bodhi tree under which the Buddha had gained enlightenment, to Sri Lanka. Messengers carried the tenets of the religion to all parts of Southeast Asia where it became entrenched. Although Buddhism was born in India, it lost ground to the mouth for three hundred years. The first resurgence of Hinduism. As a result, it is religious meeting on Buddhism was held concentrated only in pockets of the during the reign of Emperor Ashoka at Himalayas, where it survived probably because Bodhgaya, where the monastic order or of the isolation of these Sangha was founded. For the first time regions. now, texts began to be written, the earliest After the death of of them in Pali, then the common language Buddha his disciples of the people. split up in two

Emperor Ashoka was suffering remorse sects, Hinayana and after his victory in the battle of Kalinga Mahayana. Hinayana where thousands of warriors were killed. or the lesser vehicle was He sought solace in the Buddha's teach- also known as the way ings and to spread his message among his

of the elders. The followers of Hinayana strongly believe in the monastic way of life. In Hinayana teachings, the Buddha was never represented by his image; instead, he was represented by a wheel, his feet, an elephant, the bodhi tree and other such icons. Hinayana continues to have a strong following in Sri Lanka, Burma, Thailand, Laos and Cambodia.

Mahayana, the greater wheel of law, was more populist and included the worship of statues of Buddha as well as devotional rituals. This form spread far and wide, both in India and throughout the neighboring countries. In India, all the places associated with the Buddha's life continue to be major pilgrim centres, not just for the Buddhists, but among people from all walks of life, because of the peaceful nature of the religion ◆

Buddhist monks in a monastery *(opp page top);* a wall painting showing the Buddha in different mudras *(opp page center);* the crown of an Ashoka Pillar, circa 327 B.C. *(opp page bottom);* a wall painting from Ajanta showing Bodhisattva Padmapani *(left);* Buddha preaching his first sermon at Sarnath *(above);* a monk offering prayers *(right);* deers and wheel of law symbolizing Sarnath at the entrance of a Buddhist temple *(right)*

JAINISM

liberation of self from all worldly existence must be their own.

Compassion for all life, human and non human, is central to Jainism. At the heart of the religion is the belief in an extreme form of 'ahimsa' (non-violence) which demands that no living being should be hurt. For this reason, Jains are strict vegetarians, they do not eat anything that is running, swimming or flying. Even most root vegetables are avoided, as they believe this destroys the whole plant. Mahavira, last of the twenty-four tirthankars, was the greatest of all Jain ascetics and is credited with the founding of modern Jainism. He was of noble birth but gave up his luxurious family life when he was thirty. From the moment of his renunciation, he went naked and is said to have no concern for sleep, cleanliness, food or water.

Mahavira's doctrine was based upon the possibility of release from desire, suffering and death. But whereas the Buddha taught the Middle Way between luxury and asceticism, Mahavira is

The 10th Century 60 feet high image of the first tirtankar Gommateshwara in south India is a major pilgrim center for Jains *(above);* the feet of lord Mahavira cast in copper *(below);* and one of the most beautiful Jain temple in India at Ranakpur in Rajasthan *(opp page bottom)*

The word 'Jain' is derived from the Sanskrit 'jina', meaning conqueror, an epithet given to the 24 'tithankars' (prophets) who, through austerity, conquered their minds, passions and bodies to attain deliverance from the endless cycle of rebirth. Jainism is still the most ascetically demanding of all India's religions. Jains believe that salvation is achieved through ones own efforts; no guru or divinity can help you in this. In facts the devtas themselves cannot achieve liberation until they reincarnate as humans and undertake the difficult act of removing karma. Their efforts to attain permanent

famed for his severe asceticism and complete rejection of the material world. He is known as the greatest ascetic, the "most (Maha) victorious conqueror (vira)" of mind and body.

Mahavira travelled around India spreading the philosophy of non-violence. He achieved nirvana by going into deep meditation without eating or drinking anything and left his human body. Some devout Jains revere to this special practice, where in a person who is in the final stage of his life and feels that he has completed all his obligations, goes on indefinite fasting. This form of accepting death is known as Sallekhana, the person who practices it derives lot of spiritual merit. There are two main sects of Jainism — Digambar and Svetambar. The monks of the Digambar sect go completely naked. The word itself means "the one for whom the sky is the cover". They shave their heads, travel from one place to other barefoot, do not cover their bodies in blazing heat, cold, rain or sunshine. They eat only what is offered to them by their followers and that too once during the day and the amount of food eaten is what fits in their palm or fist. They never stay at one place for more than three days and the only thing they carry with them is peacock feather fans, which they use for removing insects before they sit. They also carry with them a 'kamandal' or begging bowl in which the faithful place their offerings. Any speech that incites or suggests violence must be avoided, as must

any violent tendencies in the ascetic's own thoughts. The Svetambra sect monks wear only white robes. They carry a peacock-feather brush to sweep insects from his or her path and a mask is always worn to prevent breathing in tiny organisms. Jain ascetics may not prepare food and they may only drink water that has first been strained. Garlic and onion are not used in their cooking as these are thought to bring out anger, hatred and jealousy. In stark contrast, believers of Jainism are among the wealthiest of the Indians. Because of their religion they could not be farmers, for plowing the fields would harm insects, or warriors since killing a fellow human being is sin. Hence they took to trading. And how! Today, they control the diamond and precious stone trade of the country among the many other businesses. Jainism received patronage from the Maurayan dynasty in the 3rd century B.C. There are important Jain pilgrim centres in Rajasthan (Ranakpur and Dilwara), Gujarat (Palitana). Mysore (Shravan Belgola). The popular Jain mythological stories are depicted in various temples at Jain tirthas (pilgrimage centres).The son of the first Jain prophet, Adinath, was Bahubali. When their father left home to become a

he after. Money? Property? Eventually, it was going to remain here only. Why was he fighting for material wealth? So, he renounced all his worldly possessions and started living life as an ascetic. He stood out in the open without any clothes for so long that creepers grew around his arms and legs. His hair grew long. Finally he achieved illumination and the tirtha of Shravan Belgola in Karnataka. The site now has a 17-meters tall monolithic statue of Bahubali on the hilltop.

wandering ascetic, the two brothers — Bharata and Bahubali — started fighting over the property of their father. When the fight got intense between the brothers, they came to blows. At that moment Bahubali wondered what was

Preist decorating the clothes of Lord Adinath with silver dust *(top)*; Finely carved white marble panel in Ranakpur temple showing Lord Parshvanath being given protection by Nagraj with the help of thousand hoods of cobras *(center)*; Care taker in front of Mahavira's idols *(right)*

In another story, the 23rd tirtankar, Lord Parshavanath, encounters a Sadhu

doing the five-fire penance — four fires around him and the fifth on the head. Through his divine vision Parshavnath realizes that a snake has taken refuge inside one of the burning logs and if he did not do any thing to save it, the fire would get to the reptile. He took his ax and cut open the log where the snake was trapped. The snake escaped unhurt but

The Jain temples are the cleanliest and most lovingly maintained among all Indian places of worship. They are lavishly decorated with the finest materials available. Alongside is a view of one of the 1444 richly carved columns of Ranakpur temple of which no two are alike

the sadhu's concentration was broken. The sadhu was furious with Parshavanath for disturbing his meditation. Both parted their own ways. Long after the five-fire sadhu, who now lived in heaven, saw lord Parshvanath in deep meditation on earth and decided to take his revenge. He sent so much rain that the water soon reached Parshavnath's chin. But the snake that was liberated by Lord Parshvanath was now the king of the snakes and lived in heaven; he too saw what was happening to his saviour. Consequently, king of snakes sent a message to all the snakes on earth to save

Parshvanath. Thousands of cobras rush to his rescue and lifted him by coiling their bodies around Parshvanath and saved him from drowning. With their open hoods they formed an umbrella over his head to protect him from the rain so that he could continue with his meditation.

This story is depicted in a beautiful panel of the Ranakpur temple.

The Jains as a community are only about five million-strong in India. Their respect for other life forms has left a deep impression on Indian society. Jain communities continue to support temple building - no wonder Jain temples are amongst the wealthiest and cleanest in India ◆

Guru Nanak Dev, the founder of Sikh faith, was born in the village of Talvandi, near the city of Lahore (now in Pakistan). One night he had a vision, in which God asked him to go out to the world and spread the word of love among humanity. He preached that God was in everyone irrespective to faith. God was present in all directions and was not restricted to temples, mosques and churches. Nanak stressed on kirat karo – meaning his followers should balance, work worship and charity. They should protect all living creatures especially fellow human beings. His teachings, along with the following five gurus, were recorded in the holy book of the Sikhs called Guru Granth Sahib. After his death in 1539, his followers were called the Sikhs, meaning disciples.

There were nine more Gurus following Nanak. The tenth Guru,

THE SIKHS

Guru Govind Singh initiated the Sikh baptism ceremony in the year 1699. The first five baptised Sikhs were the Panj Pyare, the five loved ones. Before his death in 1708, Guru Gobind Singh compiled the final version of Guru Granth Sahib. It contains the teachings of first five gurus and of the ninth Guru Teg Bahadur, himself; he added just one couplet to the holy scripture. He also ordained that there would be no more Gurus after him and that the holy book would be the ultimate spiritual authority of the Sikhs. Guru Granth Sahib is the only scripture in the world that has been

compiled by the founders of the faith during their lifetime. The fifth guru, Guru Arjan Dev built the Golden Temple or Darbar Sahib in the city of Amritsar, which is the temporal head of the Sikh religion.

During the eighteenth century, the Mughal emperor Aurangzeb forcibly imposed Islam religion on the Hindu masses. Guru Teg Bahadur came to their help and revolted against the Mughal ruler's atrocities. He was the youngest son of the sixth Guru, Guru Hargobind and went on to become the ninth Guru of the Sikhs. He was on his missionary tour of Bengal in east India when he heard that Aurangzeb had issued orders to forcibly convert Brahmins to Islam. Aurangzeb put five hundred Brahmins in jail hoping their plight would send a signal to the Hindu masses. The plight of the Brahmins moved the compassionate Guru who took on the might of the tyrant emperor. But Guru Teg Bahadur was arrested in Agra in 1675. From there he was brought to the Mughal court in Delhi. Aurangzeb tried to convince the Guru that Hindu idolaters should be eliminated. The Guru too was against idol worship, but loathed the idea of forced conversions and told the Emperor that these were inhuman and barbaric and were against the teachings of his Gurus.

Aurangzeb was incensed by this rebuttal. He tortured the Sikh Guru's followers and had the Guru himself beheaded in Chandni Chowk, Gurudwara Sis Ganj marks this spot. The tree under which the Muslims killed the

A Sikh gentleman with the religious insignia on his turban *(opp page top)*; pilgrims doing kar seva in the community kitchen, langar *(opp page bottom)*; the Golden Temple shimmering in the pool of nectar, Amrit Sarovar which was built by the fourth guru of the Sikhs, Guru Ram Dass during the 16th Century *(below)*; Pilgrims waiting for langar at Darbar Sahib *(above)*

Their temples are called Gurudwaras, doorway to the Guru. They worship no images, but have the holy book as their object of worship. They do not believe in the caste system, but offer community assistance in the form of kar seva. They run an open kitchen

Guru is still preserved inside this Sikh temple. Later, the body of the Guru was taken to the site where Gurudwara Rakab Ganj is situated and cremated.

The Sikhs are easily distinguishable with their colourful turbans. The turbans are about six meters long and have to be tied each time they are worn. The Sikhs believe in the five Ks and always have on their body kesh (long hair which they never cut), kanga (comb) to keep their long hair combed, kachcha (undergarment) to be ready for any eventuality, kara (steel bracelet) symbolising their unbreakable faith and kripan (knife) to fight against oppression.

called langar where anyone without the distinction of caste or creed can have food. The Sikhs are only two per cent of India's population. They are mainly concentrated in Punjab. Known for their agricultural skills, they have made their mark in all walks of life – from farming to fashion designing and from technocrats to truck drivers. They are widely accepted in India as a hard working, happy-go-lucky people ◆

Gold offered by the faithful is used to cover the domes of the Golden Temple *(top);* pilgrims resting by the pool of nectar *(above);* and the Gutka, the religious prayer book with the sacred rosary, is used for prayers at home *(below)* while the Granth Sahib, the holy book, is venerated in the Sikh temples

DYNASTY OF THE MOON GOD

In Madhya Pradesh, in central India, lies a small, sleepy village called Khajuraho. Though it has a population of no more than five thousand people, yet it boasts of an airport — the only village in India to have one. The reason , of course, are the magnificent temples, with their exquisite erotic sculptures, which were built over a thousand years ago by the rulers of the Chandela Dynasty.

While the tourist may be forgiven for mistaking these temples as primitive pornography, a close look at the sculptures will reveal the philosophy of the ancient people. As in all temples, which perform a sacred function as the home of the divine, the Khajuraho temples, too, were representation of the union of masculine and feminine energies, namely

The shikhar of the 11th Century Kandharia Mahadev temple at Khajuraho rises like a sacred mountain against the setting sun *(right);* an assistant helps a temple dancer, or devdasi, put on musical bells on her ankles before a recital before the presiding deity *(below left)*

Shiva and Shakti. For this reason the temples are decorated with erotic sculptures.

Auspicious gods, goddesses, soldiers and animals are de rigueur. But it is the amorous couples, their limbs entwined in a variety of intimate embraces which form a major composition in their own right. The sexual energy of these couples is identified with the forces of nature or the cosmic union. Indeed, the sculptures at Khajuraho signify the magical protection required to guarantee the successful life of the temple.

However, the story of the origin of the temples is more fascinating than latter day theory. Some eleven hundred years ago, so goes the tale, there lived a Brahmin priest in a village close to the jungle. He had a beautiful daughter called Hemvati. One evening, Hemvati went down to the village lake to fetch water. Since the rest of the village women had already departed after having collected water for the evening meal. The young girl decided to bathe in the cool waters of the lake since it was hot and there were no prying eyes around.

Unknown to Hemvati, Chandra, the Moon God, was entranced by her beauty and appeared beside the lakeside as a handsome prince. He seduced her and they spent the night together under the shadows of the stars. As dawn broke, the Moon God reluctantly bid

The fine craftsmanship of the Chandela temples in Khajuraho recreates scenes from the Kama Sutra. The famous frieze *(left)* shows the various positions of kama (love-making). With the advent of Muslim rulers the rigid tenets of Islam sounded the death knell of a liberal society.

farewell to take his position in the heavens. Hemvati was devastated to see him go, but Chandra told her that the son born of their union would grow up to become one of the greatest warriors of all time. He would found the Chandela dynasty that would rule for hundreds of years.

As he had prophesied, so it was. The boy Chandravarman (He who is a gift of the Moon God) grew to be powerful and rich. His dynasty built eighty-five temples in celebration of love and passion. Only twenty-two of the original temples have survived the ravages of time. Of these, the Laxman and Kandariya Mahadev temples are best conserved.

The temples are made of sandstone, which was quarried 43 kms away in Panna. Each building block was chiseled on the ground before being placed in position without the use of mortar. These were inter-locked using the tongue-and-groove method and held together by iron clamps. The carvings on the temples — of gods, goddesses, celestial dancers, amorous couples, warriors, animals and geometrical patterns are exquisite, each sensuously carved. The large quantity of sculptures has led to these temples being referred to as poetry in stone.

The temples are built on a natural foundation on the basis laid down in the ancient Indian architectural treatise called the 'Shilpa Shastra'. All the temples face east — the direction of the rising sun. The play of light and shadow on the carvings on the walls seems to give them a life-like quality. In its remote quietness, it is as if the sculptures inhabit the city of the Moon dynasty ◆

MAHATMA GANDHI

well in studies. In between, he got involved in bad company and even stole and smoked while at school. Feeling the burden of guilt, he confessed his misdeeds to his father who could not hold back his tears. This proved a pivotal point in Gandhi's life and he vowed never to waver from the path of truth.

Mohandas Karamchand Gandhi was in his early teens when his parents arranged his marriage to Kasturba. After finishing school, he sailed to England to study law. On completing his studies, he came back to

Gandhi as a young lawyer in England *(above)*; Hari Mahal, Gandhi's residence in Bombay *(right);* a prize-winning scuplture in New Delhi depicting Gandhi's famous Dandi march to protest against the obnoxious salt law *(opp page bottom)*

Gandhiji, or Bapu as he was popularly known, is one of the greatest statesmen of this century. He was born in Porbandar in Gujarat. A meek, shy child, he did not do

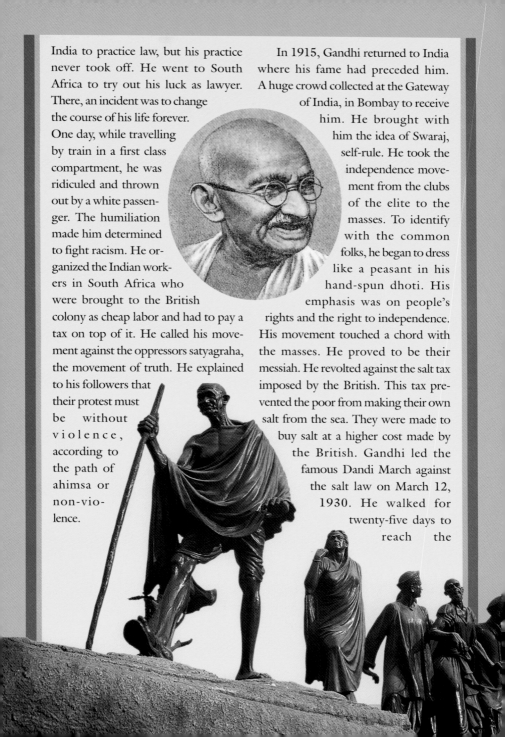

India to practice law, but his practice never took off. He went to South Africa to try out his luck as lawyer. There, an incident was to change the course of his life forever. One day, while travelling by train in a first class compartment, he was ridiculed and thrown out by a white passenger. The humiliation made him determined to fight racism. He organized the Indian workers in South Africa who were brought to the British colony as cheap labor and had to pay a tax on top of it. He called his movement against the oppressors satyagraha, the movement of truth. He explained to his followers that their protest must be without violence, according to the path of ahimsa or non-violence.

In 1915, Gandhi returned to India where his fame had preceded him. A huge crowd collected at the Gateway of India, in Bombay to receive him. He brought with him the idea of Swaraj, self-rule. He took the independence movement from the clubs of the elite to the masses. To identify with the common folks, he began to dress like a peasant in his hand-spun dhoti. His emphasis was on people's rights and the right to independence. His movement touched a chord with the masses. He proved to be their messiah. He revolted against the salt tax imposed by the British. This tax prevented the poor from making their own salt from the sea. They were made to buy salt at a higher cost made by the British. Gandhi led the famous Dandi March against the salt law on March 12, 1930. He walked for twenty-five days to reach the

The Raj Ghat, where Gandhi was cremated on the banks of the Yamuna *(left);* a postage stamp showing Gandhi and Kasturba, his wife *(below);* and the stone column which marks the spot where Gandhi was assassinated

coast. At the beginning of his journey, only a handful of followers had accompanied him, but as he marched on, thousands joined in. The satyagrahis were beaten ruthlessly, but the beatings were unable to suppress the movement against the British, which was spreading like wildfire. The British did not know how to handle a situation of non-violent protests - the satyagrahis would remain submissive even when being beaten. The civil disobedience movement paralyzed the working of the British government. Finally, the "Quit India" movement launched under the leadership of Mahatma Gandhi gained momentum. In 1947, India became independent, but another country was carved out as a separate nation: Pakistan. In 1971, one part of Pakistan liberated itself as an independent country - Bangladesh.

At the time of independence, because the division was based on religion, a civil war broke out and over a million people lost their lives. Gandhi was broken by the partition. A fanatic put an end to Gandhiji's life on January 30, 1948, barely five months after independence. His mortal remains were cremated on the banks of the river Jamuna in Delhi. Later his ashes were put in all major rivers of India.

He is best described by the scientist Albert Einstein who said that in days to come, the generations will find it hard to believe that such a man as Gandhi walked on this earth in flesh and blood ◆

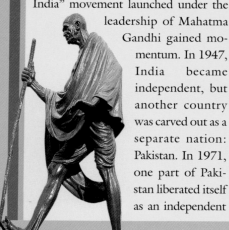

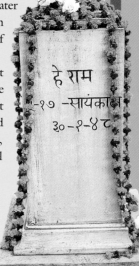

SHATRANJ -
THE GAME OF CHESS

The game of chess has an interesting origin. About 1600 years ago, there lived a king called Maharaja Ranvir who ruled the ancient kingdom of Magadh on the banks of the Ganga. The king was so inordinately fond of battles that he was forever preparing to attack, or returning from war. Not everyone in his kingdom shared his passion and his ministers were tired of his unending campaigns. Something needed to be done to wean the King away from his obsession.

So, Anantha, a reclusive Brahmin famous for his astronomy charts and mathematical calculations, was summoned by the Prime Minister and asked to find a solution. Within a week Anantha sent word to the Prime Minister that a cure would be presented in court the following morning.

At the durbar, Anantha came armed with a chequered board and thirty-two pieces of pawns and introduced the game of chess to maharaja Ranvir.

Thus there was Raja (king) in the center of the board with Senapati, or the army general on his side. They were flanked by Ashva (horse), along with Ratha (chariot), and Gaja (elephant). Foot soldiers or Paidas were placed as advancing row of pawns. The game

wish he desired.

Anantha's request seemed a simple one: He asked for just one grain of wheat for the first square of the chessboard, two for the second, four for the third, eight for the fourth, sixteen for the fifth and so on till all 64 squares were filled. The King was sure Anantha had gone senile - little did he realize that as

reflected the four-fold division of ancient Indian army, which was infantry in the first row, followed by mounted cavalry, chariots and finally, the mighty elephants. Similarly an adversary's army was created on the opposite side of the board.

The game had all the excitement and planning required in a normal battle. It captivated Ranvir and he was ready to grant Anantha any

the numbers kept doubling, just by the end of the third row, it would take 17 million grains (and 27 weeks to count them) to heed his request. If all the 64 squares were to be covered through doubling the previous count, it would take a very long time indeed to count the 1,84,46,74,40,73,70,95,51,615 grains of wheat on the last square. Clearly, Anantha was no ordinary mathematician. In fact, Anantha was

The giant chess board at the Jai Mahal garden. The chessmen were cast in solid gold and encrusted with precious stones *(left below)* for the royalty to make the right moves

finally gave up disrobing her. The great battle of Mahabharat between the cousins happens at her behest. Even though chess was invented in India, the country has not produced many world champions, for the simple reason that the rules for the game played in India are different than those for modern international chess. Under the Indian rules, the pawn's first move can be only one square as opposed to two in the modern game and the kings opposite each other and the vazirs or senapati (prime ministers or general) or queens in the modern game. And the pieces can be promoted to their own rank and don't become queens on reaching the eighth square.

appointed the finance minister of the kingdom and the king enjoyed the game of chess so much, he never went to war again.

A game of chess in progress in the streets of Udaipur. Chess is popular with Indians regardless of their social status

In ancient India, chess has been referred to by various names such as chaupar, chaturanga and ashtapadha. These games of dice have been mentioned in the Mahabharata where the Kaurava brothers tricked their cousin Pandavas into losing their kingdom and their wife, Draupadi in the game of chaupar. Intoxicated with power, the Kauravas tried to disrobe Draupadi but her honor was saved by Lord Krishna. He ensured that the saree of Draupadi was of eternal length. Tired Kauravs

Today, the popularity of the game is on the up swing once again with our own grandmasters Vishwanath Anand. Hundreds of chess tournaments held in the country are able to produce young grandmasters with regular frequency. The day is not far when young prodigies will be dominating the international tournaments ◆

BOLLYWOOD- THE HOME OF MASALA MOVIES

If one was to pick one thing that the whole nation is passionate about, it would definitely be the movies. The nation's romance with the cinema started way back in 1913, when Dadasaheb Phalke made the first silent feature film. Today, so prodigious is the output of the Hindi film industry in Bombay – hence the sobriquet Bollywood – that more than thirteen hundred films are released every year while Hollywood only manages to produce around eight hundred.

Initially, the movies were religious and patriotic: later they began confronting tough social issues such as exploitation of the farmers by the landlords, caste divisions, child marriages, and equality for women, as the backdrop for their plots. In the late 1950s, Bollywood films moved from black-and-white to color, and with it dawned the age of lavish romantic musicals and melodramas. In the following decades romance lost its luster and "*daku*" (dacoit) and later "*bhai*" (mafia don) surfaced in violent films about bandits and gangsters. The greatest film to be made in this genre was Sholay. Amitabh Bachchan, the star

known for his "angry young man" roles, rode the crest of this trend. In the early 1990s, the public was tired of violence and the pendulum swung back towards family-centric romantic musicals such as "Hum Aapke Hain Koun" (What do I mean to you?) and "Dilwale Dulhania Le Jayenge" (Romeo will take away the bride). The new millennium started with a bang with 'Kaho Na Pyar Hai' (Say I Love You) which smashed box office records and created a new superstar – Hritik Roshan. The movie's music has sold millions of copies and the film was a smash hit across the subcontinent, and in other countries of the world where it received a rapturous welcome from the expats. Indeed, the film was such a hot seller that the local Mafiosi threatened

Movies are India's passion. The film industry is driven by the movie-crazy nation to escape from the harsh reality of life. A poster of a blockbuster *(opp page);* a new generation of multiplexes are coming up in the metros *(top);* and a famous actress, Rekha peers from a movie ad

the producer for the distribution rights. He refused and was shot. But in the true Bollywood tradition, he survived.

Masala or formula movies, as these are known, follow a time-tested formula to ensure their survival at the box office. Love triangles venomously opposed by the family, corrupt politicians, hand-in-glove with the police brought to book by our hero, the dashing young police inspector. Courtesans seduce the drunk hero with their sensually suggestive dances, long-lost siblings separated by fate at birth dramatically meet up in the last shot. One dare not kill the hero or heroin as it will certainly result in a box office disaster.

The most important ingredient of the Bollywood movie is definitely the

"item number". A scantly clad actress (the "item girl"), often completely unrelated to the main plot of the film, performs a sensually enacted song with a good dose of gyrating hips and heaving of breasts. In older films, the "item number" was performed by a courtesan (tawaif) dancing for a rich client or as part of a cabaret show. Today even mainstream actresses are performing these kotha numbers, "Kajrare" song, enacted by the beautiful Aishwarya Rai is the modern version that has been a smash hit.

The Indian movie industry has a strict censor board which weeds out scenes of sex, nudity and even a passionate kiss. On the otherhand violent scenes are left untouched.

Artistic films have found audiences in multiplexes of the big cities and for the majority of the nation only the *masala* movie will do. Common man goes to the movies to escape from the harsh realities of life; real life cinema is no attraction as they live it every day.

This does not mean that serious films are not made here. In fact, the so-called parallel cinema has to its credit scores of award-winning films across the globe. Starting with Satyajit Ray, who was awarded the Oscar for Lifetime Achievement, unarguably the greatest film-maker India has produced. Lately some fabulous Bollywood movies have hit the screens, which are both artistic and *masala*. Rang de Basanti, Lage raho Munna Bhai and Omkara are the most prominent ones. Today, Shah Rukh Khan is the badshah of Bollywood. Other Khans, such as, Amir Khan, Salman Khan, Saif Ali Khan are extremely popular too. But the throne of super star is still occupied by the Big B, aka Amithabh Bachchan ◆

HIJRAS,
THE THIRD SEX

One sight that always fascinates visitors to India is groups of men dressed as women; these are 'Hijras' — castrated males (eunuchs) or those born with deformed genitals.

While elsewhere in the world eunuchs exist mostly in storybooks, in India theirs is a community of about a million-and-a-half strong and they live the life of pariahs.

Since they are neither men nor women, everyone shuns them so they live in their own community, where they find acceptance. In fact, this community has its own religion, social norms and customs. The Hijras belong to a very secretive cult dating back thousands of years, in which, childless couples would pledge their first child to the Mother Goddess and if a son was born, the parents gave him to the temple and he was castrated to keep him in her service.

Hijras refer to each other as "she" because they think of themselves as women. They prefer dressing in women's clothes, wearing jewellery and make-up. They take on female names and keep their hair long. When asked about their gender for official purposes, they write "female" which, of course, they are not. But, then, the Great Indian Bureaucracy (see above)

does not recognize a third gender. So, for official purposes — like being on the voters' list or admission to the women's wards in hospitals, instead of writing 'Hijra' they enter their gender as 'female'.

For a living, Hijras dance at festivals and celebrations — a marriage, the opening of a new shop or the birth of a new baby — for they are supposed to bring good luck. Indeed, parents and grandparents invite them to bless newborn babies. This is their tradi-tional ritualistic role for time immemorial.

According to belief, the goddess they worship — Bahuchara Mata — passes her 'shakti' (power) through them to give regenerative powers to others. One of their blessings is: "have many, many sons."

A Hijra 'Badhai' (Congratulations) song sung at weddings goes like this:

"Apple of my eyes whom I have nurtured With lots of love and affection, Today, she is grown up;

Today as my duty, I am sending her off in marriage".

There is a flip side to this — besides blessing people, they also have the power to cast a curse on them. According to one story, a train commuter used to shout abuses at a 'family' of Hijras living near the tracks. One day, their guru cast a curse on this man and a few days later he fell off the train and died. However, the good news is, even if a curse has been cast, it can be neutralized by performing a small ritual.

In fact, a fable associated with the Ramayana (but not in it) recounts a story of a group of Hijras who went, along with other citizens, to bid goodbye to Lord Rama when he left Ayodhya to go into exile for 14 years. Before his departure, the Lord also bade farewell, saying, "Men and women, go home." On his return 14 years later, he found the Hijras still waiting for him since he hadn't told them to go away. Touched by their loyalty, Lord Rama granted them the power to bless and to curse.

In the days gone by, Hindu kings used hermaphrodite servants and Muslim rulers employed castrated males. During the Muslim rule in India, they played an important part in society. They were known as Kwaja Sara and were divided into two main communities: Wazirwalla and Badshawalla. Wazirwallas served the nobility while Badshawallas had the privilege of working in the royal household. Due to their neutral sex, they were employed as harem guards with unrestricted

access to private apartments and palaces.

They were the perfect guards for, sexually, they were no threat to the women and controlled all entry into the harem. Since no outsider was permitted inside, any woman of the zenana (ladies quarters) smuggling in a lover who had the misfortune of being caught, would see him flogged to death by the Hijras. Their duties also included carrying documents and guarding the royal seal. This position gave them immense power and wealth. Many of them rose to high positions in the royal household.

Hinjra caretaker at Agra fort *(opening page)*; Three eunuchs at a roadside shrine *(opp page)*; enuchs bless the newly-wed bride Jackie after her honeymoon *(below)*; sometimes, eunuchs charge exhorbitant sums for their blessings - in this case the family had to part with fifty dollars!

Eunuch elected Mayor of Katni

PROBABLY FOR the first time in the country, Kamala Jaan, a eunuch, has been elected Mayor of a Municipal Corporation. Contesting as an independant, Kamala Jaan defeated candidates of Congress, BJP and Janata Dal (U) to emerge the winner in the civic body's election in Katni. The post was, incidentally, reserved for woman. Kamala polled 23,215 votes against 21,418 polled by Alka Jain (BJP) and 12,943 by Aradhana Jain (Congress), officials said here. **PTI, Katni**

The Hijras were very loyal to their masters. When a king was overthrown, as was quite common, they often accompanied their masters in exile and even to death. Since they were often good looking, they were often the cause of jealousy among the Muslim

princes who were bisexual. Seeing their privileged position in society, many poor parents would castrate their child in order to find employment for him in a royal household. Emperor Jehangir tried to put an end to this barbaric practice. However, the system has carried on through the ages.

In the last century, several upper class Indian homes had eunuch servants. But with the end of the princely states, eunuchs found themselves without status and employment. With royal patronage coming to an end, the Hijras withdrew into ghettos in the walled quarter of old towns.

However, according to some of them, the family planning program in the country has made things difficult for them. And since, given their pariah status, jobs are hard to come by and they have been reduced to begging to make ends meet. Hard times have also driven many into prostitution.

Hijras belong to all faiths but are joined together in their worship of 'Bahuchara Maa'. The main temple of the goddess is located at Bechraji, a small town north of Ahmedabad in Gujarat and the priests are male Brahmins. The goddess 'Bahuchara Maa' usually rides a rooster so there are several live ones in the temple grounds. Worshippers can promise to set a rooster free if their petitions to the goddess are granted. Old eunuchs, supported by the temple spend their days around it. There is a statue of the goddess in silver. She changes her vehicle daily according to the manifestation — she could also ride a lion, peacock, swan, tiger, bull or elephant.

The temple was built 700 years ago near the grounds of Maharaja Manekji Gaekwad's palace. As legend has it, the King, while on a hunt one day, found himself caught in a river of long hair. He followed it saw it belonged to the serene goddess Bahuchara Maa who was on a swing. The king fell in love with her. "You are very beautiful," he declared. "Will you marry me?"

"Yes," she answered, "but not today. Come on Tuesday with jewellery and food and I will marry you."

The king rode there on the appointed day with his guests and even his dog. "Take a dip in the water and refresh yourself first," the goddess ordered. As he submerged himself in the tank — which still exists — she said, "Now look at yourself."

The king was stunned — his penis had vanished!

"How did this happen," he asked incredulously. "No one can marry me," she proclaimed, "for I am your mother and you are my son. After you, there will be others like you. You will take care of them; I will give you the power to grant fertility to others."

"But won't men die if you cut off their organs?" the king asked.

"Look at your dog," she said and ordered the dog and then the horse into the water. They, too, lost their organs. The dog yelped in pain.

"Take some hot oil and hot water and put it on the incision," she ordered. The dog became quiet and survived. "This method is for everyone," she said. "You will not die." This ritual method of castration — known as 'nirvana' — is practiced even today.

Since then, men in this temple sing, "Why don't you make us a Hijra like the king?"

For most Hijras today, their natural families have been replaced by Hijra families. These 'families' are groups of well-organized believers who help and protect each other. About seven to fifteen of them are joined together in one unit and each family is headed by a 'guru'. They call each other 'sister', 'daughter', 'aunt' or 'mother-in-law'.

Each guru, in turn, belongs to an elder called 'nayak' and groups of nayaks oversee and decide the territory in which the Hijras work. The guru takes care of her flock and is given part of the earnings. Hijras do not necessarily live with their gurus. Many live alone while some even have male husbands and work as homemakers.

It would not be long before the changing times wrap the tradition of the hijras into the folds of history. As new economics is making the families smaller and the timeless traditions impractical ◆

Eunuch elected to MP assembly

The Times of India News Service

BHOPAL: Voters in the Sohagpur assembly constituency in Shehdol district in Madhya Pradesh created history of sorts on Friday by electing Shabnam Mausi, a eunuch, as their MLA in the bypolls held on February 17.

Contesting as an independent, Shabnam Mausi defeated her closest rival, Lallu Singh of the BJP, by 17,863 votes. Shabnam got 39,937 of the 1,02,382 votes polled. There were nine candidates in the fray. Congress nominee Brijesh Singh, son of former Gujarat governor Krishnapal Singh, came a poor third.

Shabnam Mausi (40) was born in Mumbai to a Brahmin family. Father Gokul Prasad Sharma is a retired deputy inspector-general of police and said to be living in Kanpur. Shabnam, who left home at the age of 11, has been living for the past 20 years in Anuppur in Shehdol and makes a living by singing and dancing. Shabnam speaks 11 languages, including English, Hindi, Marathi, Gujarati, Punjabi, Kannada, Telegu and Tamil. Checking unemployment and rising prices top her agenda as MLA.

MANIKARNIKA:
THE BURNING GHAT

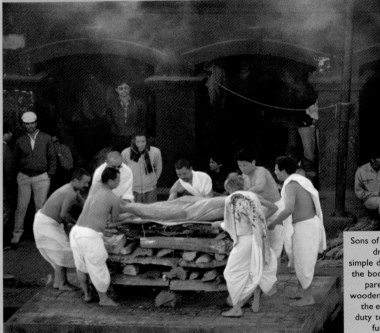

Sons of the family dressed in a simple dhoti place the body of their parent on the wooden pyre. It is the eldest son's duty to light the funeral pyre

According to Hindu legend, Lord Shiva performed a demanding penance on the banks of river Ganges in his favourite city, Varanasi. His endeavour was to uplift the plight of living beings of this world who were trapped in 'Samsara' or the cycle of birth and re-birth. His meditation or tapasya was so powerful that the ground where he performed it became hollow. Lord Vishnu was very pleased with Lord Shiva's devotion and compassion for living beings. He appeared in person where Lord Shiva was meditating to grant him a boon. It is said that Lord Shiva asked him to grant salvation to all human beings who came to the holy city of Varanasi during their lifetime. Lord Vishnu was pleased with Lord Shiva's empathy and granted him the

boon. As an after-thought, Lord Shiva requested Lord Vishnu to also liberate those who came to the city as corpses from the cycle of birth and re-birth and award them moksha. As an affectionate gesture Lord Vishnu took Lord Shiva's face in his hands and shook it. The earring on the ear of Lord Shiva dislodged and fell down to the ground. This very spot where the earring fell was named Manikarnika (mani = jewel + karnika = of the ear) and the place where Lord Shiva performed the penance is the small pond behind it.

Manikarnika Ghat is also known as

the 'Burning Ghat'. Since the dawn of history, dead bodies have been brought for cremation to this holy spot. This tradition is as old as the city itself. And Varanasi, it is said, is the oldest living city in the world … older than the legends. Since Manikarnika Ghat has been sanctified by Lord Vishnu and Lord Shiva, the cremation here has a special significance as it assures the departed soul liberation from the cycle of birth and re-birth.

Every day about 150 cremations take place at this maha shamshan or great crematorium round the clock, but the cremation ground gets more crowded in the afternoon as the residents from the nearby villages start to arrive with the dead bodies.

The body of the deceased is washed clean before being wrapped in the

Manikarnika or the burning ghat receives the bodies round the clock. At night, the huge orange flames consuming the mortal remains is an impressionable sight. *(below)* A Dom or caretaker of the funeral pyre shifts the logs with the pole to ensure that no parts of the body remain un burnt

shroud and tied to a small ladder made out of bamboo. Pall-bearers are the male members of the family who carry the body on their shoulder reciting, "Ram Nam Satya Hai" or "Lord Rama's name is the real truth", all the way to the cremation ground.

On the way to the cremation ghat the police check-post registers the details of the dead person and later issues the death certificate. On reaching the cremation ground the family hands over the body to 'Doms' or caretakers.

'Doms' belong to the lowest of the low caste of the Hindu caste system and traditionally work in the cremation grounds. 'Doms' guide the family on how much wood (around 300 kg) to buy for the ceremony. Camphor and clarified butter are the only other inflammable materials used in the cremation.

The dead body is first dipped in the Ganges River for purification and left to dry on the steep steps of the ghat. The eldest son of the departed

direction to symbolize the return of the body to the five elements of the nature.. He then buys the holy fire from 'Raja Dom', or the king of 'Doms' and lights the pyre with the burning grass. Raja Dom alone is the custodian of the eternal sacred fire used for the cremation. There is no fixed charge

performs the rites of self-purification. His head is shaved clean and he wears white cloth around his body. In the meanwhile, the family members buy the religious merchandize needed for performing the last rites. 'Doms' build the pyre according to the size of the body, the majority of the wooden logs are placed below the body and the rest are used to cover the top and the sides.

The eldest son (or in his absence eldest male member) walks around the pyre five times in anti-clockwise for the fire; depending on the person's economic status, he extracts money.

The whole ritual is carried out in silence because it is believed that expressing grief may disturb the transmigration of the soul. For this very reason, womenfolk do not come to the cremation ground.

Family members wait for the body to turn into ashes, which takes about three hours. The exploding of the skull

symbolizes the release of the soul. Later, all pall-bearers go for a holy dip in the river Ganges before returning to their homes. After the body has completely burnt the smouldering ashes are collected by the 'Doms' and put into the river to make room for the new arrival. The Hindus, who are not cremated on the banks of the Ganges, their ashes are collected on the next day of the cremation and taken by the male members of the family to be immersed in the river Ganges.

Children below the age of ten years are not cremated as they are considered to be immature. They are instead immersed into the river with a stone tied around their body. Sadhus and yogis also are not cremated but given Jal Samadhi or buried in the water as they are considered to have surpassed the human level of existence. Lepers are not cremated so as not to anger fire god whose repercussions would be more persons suffering from the same disease. People who die of snakebite too are not cremated. Their body is tied to a raft made from banana trunks and made to float on the Ganges River. Since snakes are associated with Lord Shiva, their bite is considered auspicious hence they do not need to be cremated. Pregnant women too are not cremated, as the baby in their womb is not yet formed.

Thirteen days after the cremation, Brahmins are invited by the family of the deceased and fed. Elaborate religious rites are performed by the family members to mark the completion of transmigration of the soul from earth to heaven ◆

GANGA: THE CELESTIAL RIVER GODDESS

Godess Ganga was the daughter of the mighty Himayan and Mena. Her maternal grand father was the mythological Mountain Meru. Since her childhood, Ganga was very vivacious. Each time she wandered away from home, she took form of a river. The mighty Himalayas loved and tolerated her mischief. One day, Devtas (gods) came down from heaven to roam the mountains where they saw Ganga, playing around. They were impressed with her youthful energy. They went to see her

A Hindu ascetic dressed in the holy beads of rudrakshas and holding a trident, a symbol of lord Shiva, meditates to the rising sun

father and convince him to send her
with them to heaven. Himayan was
very pleased that the Devtas thought
her fit enough to be invited to swarglok
or heaven and readily gave his consent.

In heaven the Devtas were inspired
by her presence and their popularity
started to grow ten folds. But the
demons could not stomach their
growing popularity and decided to
attack them. Lord Indira, king of the

(left); A Bhramin
performs the
evening aarti on
the banks of the
river Ganges.
(right) Panoramic
view of the ghats of
Varanasi that are full
of life. A boat cruise
is the best way to
soak in its beauty.
(below) A pilgrim
offers the water
of Ganges to the
rising sun

Devtas fought bravely against the
demons, defeated them badly and
pushed them to the bottom of the
ocean.

Here the demons regrouped and
at night started killing all the religious
people. There was total anarchy. As the
result, Gods became weak and listless.
Event Ganga could do little to boost
their morale.

A delegation of Devtas went to
consult Lord Vishnu who though his
divine vision knew that the demons
were hiding at the bottom of the ocean.
Vishnu however suggested that they

use the experience of sage Agatsaya
as he had the unique power to dry
up the ocean.

Sage Agatsaya was more than happy
to assist the Devtas and went to the
ocean and drank it. As soon as the
demons were exposed the Devtas
eliminated them though a few escaped
by hiding under the floor of the ocean.
Devtas now turned to sage Agatsaya
and with folded hands requested him
to refill the ocean. Agatsaya expressed
his helplessness as he has already
digested the water. This calamity, the
Devtas were not ready for; their

delegation once again knocked door of Lord Bhrama and explained the problem that loomed in front of mankind. He predicted, "The oceans will fill up when childless Sagar, the king of Ayodhya will have children. While this drama was going on in heaven, on earth, sage Bhrigu was pleased by the penance of king Sagar and his two wives. The sage prophesized that one wife will give birth to a son while the second wife will give birth to 60,000 sons. The sage's prophecy did come true and the elder queen gave birth to a son

while younger one found sixty thousand little boys when she cut open the fruit of gourd.

King Sagar's son turned out to be incapable of ruling hence the throne was passed on to his grandson. The group of sixty thousand children from the second wife turned out to be arrogant. When their father lost his sacrificial horse, he asked them to go look for it. In their pursuit they reached sage Kapilas hermitage where they found the horse grazing. Their arrogance thought nothing of disturbing sage Kapila's meditation and added insult to injury

calling him a thief. Sage Kapila's fiery eyes turned 60,000 children of king Sagar to ashes.

Finally, it was the great great grandson of Sagar, Bhagirath who came to the rescue. Bhagirath abandoned the luxuries of the kingdom and prayed for years with his arms raised for the Ganges to come down from the heaven and flow over the ashes of his uncles. His penance of five fires and meditation pleased the gods who came down to grant him a boon. Bhagirath requested goddess Ganges to come on earth. Brahma agreed but the problem was if Ganges was to descend directly on earth then the world would split into two with the force of the fall. Lord Shiva was then requested to break the fall of the Ganges by receiving her in his matted hair. All the Devtas came to watch the divine spectacle of the Ganges descending on the earth and flow over the ashes of sixty thousands son of Sagar to liberate them. Maa Ganga or Mother Ganges washes away the sins of all beings with her pure waters ◆

Young Brahmins gather on the banks of Ganges in Rishikesh for the evening ceremony. *(below)* A bhramin holds aloft a lamp of burning camphor as an invocation to the river goddess ganges in Varanasi

SPICE OF LIFE

India is a land of extremes where the rich are very rich and the poor, very poor. And our sense of smell too is pervaded by extremes – wonderful rich aromas or positively foul odours! Similarly in our food the tastes are very marked, sweet becomes very sweet and spicy, very spicy.

Indian food is as varied as the landscape and languages of the country. Each geographical region boasts of its variety of delicacies and added to this each caste, linguistic and religious group have their own dietary laws which have been strictly adhered to generation after generation.

In some castes and religious groups it is acceptable to eat meat while in others the only non-vegetarian food permitted is eggs. Added to this there are grades of distinction between vegetarians; some religious groups prohibiting the use of onion and garlic in the preparation of their food, while in coastal areas fish is accepted as part

of a vegetarian diet. Beef is consumed only in areas where there is a high concentration of Muslim and Christians. Hindus, because of their religious sentiments do not eat beef.

Spices are at the heart of all Indian cooking and Europeans since the Middle Ages have been attracted to India's shores by the lure of them; apart from the wealth they accumulated from importing and selling, the use of spices to conserve their meat due to lack of refrigeration in Europe was an important part of their living. India's eating habits are by and large biased towards a vegetarian diet of which there is a tremendous variety. In South India dosa, idli and sambhar are the regional dishes; in North India, dal, roti and tandoori cooking are popular. Fish curry and rice are the staple diets of the East. All are eaten with great relish

and the hotter the region within the country the more fiery the curries! Unlike the western world where food is prepared using ready-mixes each time a dish is cooked, all the spices are freshly ground and prepared for the appropriate dish and different spices used depending on the dish to be cooked.

Indians mostly eat from a large

stainless steel plate called a Thali. It has numerous partitions for the any variety of curry, dals (lentils), subzi (vegetables) and raita (yoghurt with cucumber or onion). Roti (unleavened bread) and rice is put into the middle

of the thali along with achar (pickle). On festival occasions the number of different dishes may be as many as 7 or 10 while a normal everyday meal consists of 2 or 3 variations of vegetables, lentils and yoghurt. There is no second course, everything is served at the same time and Indians really enjoy the variations in taste and with each different meal savour and discuss the merits of the food they are eating!

No cutlery is used, everyone eats by hand but in modern households one does find extensive use of cutlery.

Salad, if any, comprises of onions, tomatoes and cucumber to which is added lemon, salt, pepper and red chilli powder. In Indian culture it is not customary to drink alcohol with food. If it is consumed, then it is before meals. As soon as dinner is over people tend to leave; after-dinner drink, tea or coffee are a rarity.

The streets of India are famous for their authentic wayside cooking but they are not for the faint hearted! There are many varieties of snacks and meals to be enjoyed on the street corner. Restaurants even try to imitate the humble pushcart on the street. But

Red chillies dry out in the farm after the harvest. These will be dried and then sold to be crushed into powder to add to the curries.
(below) a halwai deep frying spicy pastry called katchori

nothing beats the real thing. Some of these delicious delicacies are: Matka Chana (boiled peas served with an amalgamation of spices); Kulche Chole (chick peas with thick dark gravy served with fluffy bread); Batata Wada (tempura of spiced boiled potatoes served in a bun); Pani Puri (golf ball sized puffed pastry that is served with spiced mint water along with spicy stuffing of potatoes and chic

peas); Bhel Puri (puffed rice served with sweet and sour sauce along with boiled potatoes, onions, tomatoes and sprinkled with crackers). This is the most common street food and is best enjoyed on the streets. Restaurants have now started to imitate street food but they don't have the taste and ambiance of pushcarts on the street corner.

But the king of street food is Mirchi Vada (chilli tempura), prepared by the roadside eateries of Jaipur, Jodhpur and Udaipur in Rajasthan. The preparation is really quite simple: a healthy-sized green chilli is cut open in the middle and stuffed with spicy boiled potatoes. It is then dipped into the thick paste made out of the chickpea flour and deep fried in mustard oil. Once the batter turns golden brown in colour, the Mirchi Vada is taken out and served with sweet and sour sauce.

Well prepared Mirchi Vada is simply out of this world. A bite into a it sends a wake up call to all dormant taste buds and virtually flames leap out of your mouth! It is rounded up with a cup of sweet masala tea that douses

(above left); Close up of katchories and dal ki pakori in the frying pan. *(above center)* Variety of spices used in Indian cusine. *(above right and below)* Samosa, (a pyramid of spicy potatoes with herbs encased in thin batter and deep fried), for sale in various halwai shop

the fire within.

Street food is safe as long as it is clean and eaten hot; 'Delhi belly' the euphemism for an upset stomach, can be avoided if the food is prepared in a clean environment and eaten piping hot. To be doubly sure that nothing goes wrong on the morning after, a glass of lassi (yogurt churned with water with a touch of salt and pepper) should be taken. Paan or beetle leaf is consumed in the end of the meal to ged rid of heavy aromas of the Indian food. The downside is that it leaves the mouth and tongue dark red in colour ◆

A

Abul Faizal - most trusted courtier of Akbar

Achar – spicy vegetable conserves served with India food

Achkan - long coat with mandarin collars

Adinath - first of the 24 Jain prophets

Adi Shankracharya - one of the most revered saints of India, he is responsible of revival of Hinduism in the 8th century, he also established four maths, in the four cardinal directions of India

Agra - city of Taj Mahal, was the capital of the Mughal empire from the 16th till the 17th century

Ahimsa – non-violence

Ajana Chakra - last of the six energy centers, it is located on the forehead

Akbar - third and the greatest ruler of the Mughal dynasty, builder of Agra Fort and Fatehpur Sikri

Akhara - Indian gym or place where sadhus reside

Amer - old capital of Jaipur city

Amir – noble

Amrit – nectar

Anarkali - a common dancing girl who's love affair with prince Salim shook the Mughal throne

Andhka - a demon

Arjuna - bravest of the five Pandavas

Aryan - the race of north India

Asana - various yogic positions

Ashoka Pillar - monolithic polished granite columns which have edicts of Buddhism engraved, erected by emperor Ashoka in 327 B.C. it's capital is now the national symbol

Ashtanga yoga – eight school of yoga

Ashtpad - eight moves

Atman - the eternal soul

Ayodhya - kingdom of Lord Rama, hero of the epic Ramayana

B

Babur - founder of Mughal dynasty in India

Bali - a demon

Bahrupia - man of many appearances

Bapu - father, Mahatma Gandhi was often addressed by this name

Batata vada – tempura of boiled potatoes served with spicy sauce and bun

Bhagirath - saint whose prayers resulted in the goddess Ganges descending from the heaven in form of a holy river

Bhai – literally means brother but in slang means mafias worker or mafia don

Bhel puri – toasted rice mixed with onions and tomatoes and loaded with spicy sauce

Bhikshu - a Hindu or a Buddhist monk

Bhim - strongest of the five Pandava brothers

Bhishti - traditional water carrier, who use goats skin for the purpose of dispensing water

Bindi - decoration on the forehead of Indian women

Birbal - one of the most famous Hindu ministers of Akbar

Bodhi tree - tree of knowledge, under which Gautam reached illumination

Bodhgaya - place where Gautama reached illumination

Bodhisattva - future Buddha

Brahma - first God of Hindu trinity, the Creator

Brahmacharya - the period of life as student abstaining from sex and intoxicants

Brahmin - the first caste of the priests in the Hindu society

Buddha - the illuminated one, term used for Gautama or Sakyamuni

C

Chakra - energy centers along the spine

Chamar - Cobblers belonging to a low caste who skin dead animals

Chamundi - goddess in destructive form

Chandela - dynasty of the moon god who built the famous Khajuraho temples
Chandra - moon god
Chandravarman - son of the moon god
Charbag - typical Mughal garden divided in four by water channels
Chaturanga - the four sided dice game of ancient India, it finally evolved into modern day chess

D

Dal – popular Indian soup made of wide variety of lentils
Dalit - low caste
Daku – robber or bandit who lives in the country
Devdasi - temple dancer
Devta – God or demigod
Dhanvantri - ancient art of living and healing
Dharma - religion and social conduct for Hindus, Jains and the Buddhist
Dhritrashtra - father of Kauravas
Dhyan - to concentrate, to meditate
Dhobi - laundry man
Digambar - "sky clad" Jain monks who live without clothes
Din-i-Ilahi - Akbar's experiment treating all religions as equal
Diwali - most important Hindu festival, it marks the return of Rama to Ayodhya after 14 years of exile
Diwan-i-Am - hall of public audience
Diwan-i-Khas - hall of private audience
Doli - palanquin which carries the bride after the marriage to her husband's home, nowadays replaced by cars
Dosa – south Indian crepe made out of rice and lentils
Draupadi - common wife of five Pandava brothers
Dravadian - original race of India now concentrated in the south
Durbar – court

Duryodhan - jealous cousin of the Pandavas

E

Ek Danta - one tooth, name used for lord Ganesha
Eunuchs - third sex, castrated males or those born with deformed genitals

F

Fatehpur Sikri - abandoned city near Agrabuilt by third Mughal emperor, Akbar
Fergana - the birth place of Babur, founder of the Mughal dynasty in India, it is located in modern day Uzbekistan
Firman - court document during the Mughal period
Five K's – Kesh (hair); Kripan (knife); Kanga (comb); Kachha (under garment); Kara (steel bangle) symbols that Sikhs must carry with them

G

Gali - a narrow street
Gandhiji - Gandhi, father of the nation, architect of India's independence, popularised non violent form of protest.
Ganga - the sacred river of India
Gaudan - gifting of the cows to the priest after a religious ceremony
Gaumukh - mouth of cow, source of the river Ganges
Gautam - name of Buddha
Gopal - keeper of cows, popular name of lord Krishna
Gopis - village beauties who were at a receiving end of lord Krishna's affection
Grihastha Ashram - period of life when one raises a family
Guna - good qualities in a person
Guptas - the Hindu dynasty of the 4th century popularly known as the India's renaissance
Guru - teacher, the one who shows you the path, could be of philosophy, yoga, dance, music etc

Guru Granth Sahib - holy book of the Sikh religion, it compiles the teachings of all the ten gurus

Gurukul - boarding school of ancient India where students lived with the guru in his formative years

H

Hakim - doctor in medieval times

Hamida Bano - also known as Bega Begum, she was mother of Akbar and builder of Humayun's tomb

Hanuman - the monkey god who helped Lord Rama in his battle against the demon king Ravana

Harem - part of the palace where the women lived

Harijan - "children of God", term used by Mahatma Gandhi to address the low caste

Hatha Yoga - one of four main schools of yoga involving physical exercises

Himalaya - the temple/house of snow, highest mountain chain in the world

Hinayana - "The way of the elders" school of Buddhism stressing on monastic way of life

Hindustan - the land on the other side of the river Indus, name of India in medieval period

Hijras - Eunuchs or hermaphrodites

Holi - hindu festival of colour

Humayun - second Mughal emperor, he lies buried in Humayun's tomb in Nizamuddin area of Delhi

I

Ibrahim Lodhi - ruler of the Lodhi dynasty who was killed by Babur, the founder of Mughal empire, in the battle of Panipat

Idli – steamed rice cakes, popular south Indian breakfast

Imabatkhana - house for discussions of the religious philosophies

Indra - the rain god

J

Jain - minority religion of India which respects all types of life forms

Jama Masjid - the friday mosque

Janampatri - a scroll depicting the positions of the planets as interpreted by the family Brahmin at the time of the birth

Jata - Sadhu's dread locks

Jatayu - a vulture who fought with the demon Ravana

Jaya – victory

Jharokha - window from where king would appear in the public

Jazia - tax on non muslims

Jihad - holy war in name of Islam

Jina – conqueror

Juna Akhara - sect of the sadhus

Jyoti - flame of knowledge

K

K's of the Sikhs - 1.Kanga (comb) 2. Kripan (dagger) 3. Kaccha (undergarment) 4. Kesh (long hair) 5. Kara (steel bracelet).

Kalidasa - the great Indian poet of 4th century

Kalinga - kingdom in eastern India

Kalyuga - dark age when wrong rules the right

Kamandal - a bowl carried by the holy men in which the offerings are placed

Kamdhenu - cow that fulfills desire

Kans - a demon out to kill baby Krishna

Karma – destiny shaped by the actions of past life

Karseva - voluntary work carried out by the Sikhs

Kasturba - wife of Gandhi

Kauravas - 100 brothers who fought Pandava brothers in the battle of Mahabharata

Kesari - saffron color

Khichri - a dish made out of rice and lentils cooked together

Kirat karo – to do charity work for others

Kotha – brothel where girls lure customers by dancing

Kshatriya - second caste of the Hindus, belonging to the warrior and ruling class
Kumbh Mela - celebrated every 12 years, it has biggest gathering of the Indian holy men
Kumra - tortoise incarnation of lord Vishnu
Kundalini - the dormant energy at the base of the spine
Kurukshetra - the place where the battle of Mahabharata was fought

L

Lanka - kingdom of the demon king Ravana
Langar - communal meals served at the Sikh temples
Laxman - brother of lord Rama
Laxmi - the goddess of wealth
Lehenga - skirt worn by Indian women especially at weddings
Lingam - phallus representation of Lord Shiva
Lota - small water pot
Lumbini - birthplace of lord Buddha

M

Mahabharata - the epic war between Pandavas and their cousins Kauravas
Mahal – palace
Maharaja - King of Kings
Maharani - wife of Maharaja
Mahavira - last of the Jain prophets
Mahayana - the great wheel of law, the second Buddhist sect
Mahayogi - one who has mastered Yoga
Mahout - the elephant rider
Makrana - town close to Jaipur where the white marble for the Taj Mahal was mined
Malabar - western coast of India
Mangal – auspicious
Manglik - those born under the influence of the planet Mars
Manthan - churning of the oceans by the demons and the Gods
Manu - the first human in Hindu mythology
Marwar - land of the dead, Jodhpur state
Masala – spices or amalgamation of various spices

Masala tea – tea prepared with ginger, clove, cardamom and other spices
Masala movie – typical Indian movie with songs, fights, rapes and dramatic emotions
Mast - when elephants go out of control
Math - religious centers
Matka chana – cooked chickpeas served with spicy sauces from bronze pots
Matsya - fish incarnation of lord Vishnu
Maya – illusion
Mela – fair
Mewar - kingdom of the proud Maharanas
Mirchi vada – tempura of hot chlli
Mishri - crude sugar crystals
Mithuna - copulating figures of Khajuraho temples
Mithai - Indian sweets
Moksha – liberation
Moolah - money
Mubarak – greetings
Mudra - gestures conveying message
Muezzin - one who calls for prayers
Mughal - Muslim dynasty which ruled India between the 16th and the 18th century
Mysore - state in southern India famous for sandal wood

N

Nadis - energy channels
Naga – cobra
Nakul - one of the Pandava brothers
Namaste - Indian greeting
Nanak - founder of the Sikh religion
Nandi - the bull, official vehicle of lord Shiva
Nara – water
Narasimha - incarnation of lord Vishnu as half-man and half-lion
Narayan - lord Vishnu
Neelkanth - one with the blue throat - lord Shiva
NRI - Non Resident Indian, expats

O

Om - cosmic sound used in prayer and

meditation
Omkar - lord Shiva

P

Padma – lotus
Padmapani - Bodhisttava with lotus
Padmasana - the lotus pose
Pali - ancient Indian language
Panda - Brahmin, priest
Pandava - five brothers, heroes of the epic Mahabharata
Panj Pyaare - first five disciples of Guru Govind Singh who were baptized to the Khalsa Panth
Panipat - town 70 km north of Delhi where the Lodhi dynasty lost to the Mughals
Pashupati – the lord of flora fauna another name for Lord Shiva
Parshuram - 6th incarnation of lord Vishnu
Parsvanath - 23rd Jain prophet, his statues are decorated with cobra hood
Pavan - the wind god
Pheras - the rounds taken at the time of marriage with fire as the testimony
Porbandar - small town in Gujarat where Gandhiji was born
Prana - life giving force
Pranayam - breathing yogic exercise
Prayag - confluence of the rivers Ganga, Jamuna and Saraswati in the city of Allahabad
Prithvi - earth goddess
Puja - religious ceremony of the Hindus
Punjab - fertile region of north India, homeland of the Sikhs and the Punjabis
Puranas - ancient scriptures of Hinduism
Pushkar - pilgrim center famous for the Brahma temple and annual camel fair

Q

Quila – fort
Quila Mubarak - Red Fort of Delhi built by Shah Jahan, the fifth Mughal emperor

R

Rahul - son of Buddha
Raita – beaten yogurt mixed with some raw vegetable
Raja - king, administrator
Raja Yoga - school of Yoga
Raj Ghat - memorial of Gandhi in Delhi where he was cremated
Raj Tilak - coronation ceremony of Maharaja
Rajput - the warrior clan of western India
Ramayana - greatest of the Hindu epics
Rana - warrior clan of Nepal
Rana Sangha - brave ruler of Mewar who refused to cow down in front of the Muslim armies
Rangeela - nickname of Mohamed Shah, ruler of Delhi, who indulged in wild parties even under attack
Rangoon - capital city of Burma
Ravana - demon king of Sri Lanka
Roti - Indian bread made from wheat flour
Rudra - Shiva when angry

S

Sabha & Samiti - village community of the elders
Sadhu - Indian holy man
Sahdev - one of the five Pandava brothers
Sakya - clan of Buddha
Salim Chishti - Sufi saint who's blessing gave childless emperor Akbar an heir to the throne, Prince Salim. Akbar got Fatehpur Sikri built as mark of respect and shifted his capital there for 13 years
Sambhar – spicy lentil soup served with south Indian food
Samadhi – memorial
Samagri - different objects which are needed in a Hindu religious ceremony
Samarkand - the former capital of the Mughals
Samsara – world in which we live
Sangha - religious gathering of the Buddhist monks
Sanskrit - ancient Indian language of the

priests, said to be the mother of all Indo European languages

Saraswati - goddess of learning, wife of lord Brahma

Sari - Indian dress for women

Sarnath - Deer Park where Buddha gave his first sermon

Satyagraha - non violent movement against the British started by Gandhi

Sesha Naga - thousand headed cobra, also serves as lord Vishnu's bed

Sevadar - Sikh in community service

Shah Jahan - the fifth ruler of the Mughal dynasty and the builder of Taj Mahal

Shahi snan - royal bath of sadhus during the Kumbh festival

Shakti - manifestation of female energy as destructive force

Shankh - conch shell one of Vishnu's attributes

Shariyat - muslim law

Sher Shah Suri - Afghan ruler of Bengal who overthrew Humayun – the second Mughal emperor

Shikar – hunt

Shikhar - Hindu temple spire under which main deity of the temple is housed

Shilpa Shastra - ancient texts on architecture

Shiva - third god of Hindu trinity, lord of destruction and creation

Sindh - region of south Pakistan

Sindoor - red powder put by married ladies in the parting of their hair

Sisganj - Sikh temple in old Delhi where the 9th guru was beheaded by Mughal emperor Aurangzeb

Sita - wife of lord Rama

Subzi – generic term for raw and cooked vegetables

Sufi - mystic sect of the Muslims

Suhaag Raat - first night after marriage

Sultanate - the period of Indian history between 14th and 16th century

Surabhi - cow of plenty

Sura – demon

Surya - the sun god

Svetambara - sect of Jain monks dress in white

T

Tansen - classical singer during Akbar's reign

Tapasvi - person undergoing penance

Tandoori – something that is cooked in vertical clay oven called tandoor

Tawaif – Call girl who makes her living by dancing for men

Thali – circular plate on which food is served in India

Thangka - Buddhist painting showing mandalas

Tilak - marking on the forehead after a religious ceremony

Tirtha - pilgrim center

Tirthankara - prophet of the Jains

V

Valmiki - translated the epic Ramayana from sanskrit to the common man's language

Vanar Sena - army of the monkeys who joined the army of lord Rama

Vanaprastha ashram - stage of life when one abandons all comforts and goes to live in a jungle

Varmala - flower garlands exchanged between the bride and the groom

Varna - color, caste

Vazir – minister

Vedas - ancient Indian texts – books of knowledge

Vedic Period - when Vedas were written.

Vibhuti - sacred ash

Vishnu - lord of preservation, second God of the Hindu trinity

Z

Zenana - part of the house or palace were women lived

INDEX

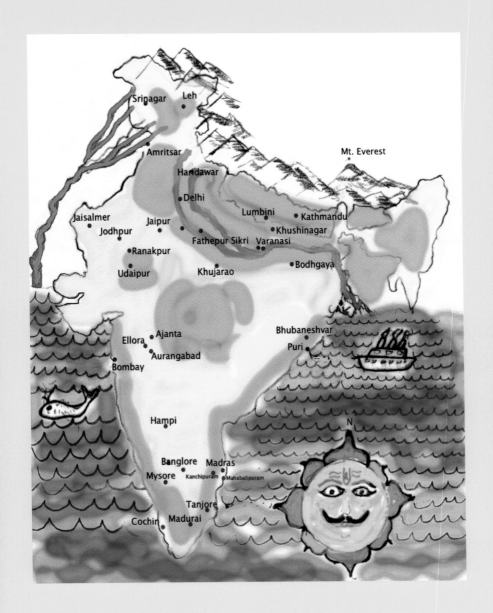